Farmer's Diary

Charlie Allan

Illustrations by
Turnbull

Ardo Publishing Company
Methlick, Aberdeenshire AB41 0HR

I am grateful to the *Herald* for permission
to reproduce these articles, which first appeared
in print in that newspaper.

Published by Ardo Publishing Company, Buchan

*© Copyright 1994. Not to be reproduced
in any form without permission.*

Printed in Great Britain by BPC Wheatons Ltd, Exeter

Foreword

YOU MIGHT think that the production of this third volume would indicate that the previous two had been a great success. You could be forgiven for thinking Volume Three a sign that the Farmer is, in fact, rolling in it.

Several things could be further from the truth...but not much.

In fact Volume Two has been, as the auctioneering houses say, stiffer to cash, and the old farmhouse is still full of them. But the funny thing is that, when Volume Two came out, there was a rush for the remaining copies of Volume One. The production of this third collection is provoked by the desperate hope that it will cause a rush for Volume Two.

In fact I fear that I may be on something of treadmill. It may be necessary to produce a fourth volume in order to shift this one.

I am again indebted to Jim Turnbull for his cartoons which make these articles palatable to so much wider an audience. I particularly admire the way he manages to see aspects of what has been written that I have not seen myself.

The Breadwinner has done all the desk-top publishing on Volume Three in the time she has left over from her job in the toon, doing the cooking here, explaining to people that she really doesn't know when I'll be in and being the farm's accountant. I am also indebted to Sarah Purdie who read the proofs and pointed out a lot of mistakes in grammar and spelling overlooked by our unimaginative computer. She must not be blamed for remaining mistakes because I insist on some eccentricities.

We've tried a new system in the printing of this book whereby we give a computer disk to a firm called BPC-AUP, they plug it into a machine and the books, neatly wrapped in tens, come out the other end almost instantly, along with the invoice. We are grateful to Murray Webster and his team for their patience in coping with our inexperience but if we don't like the result we intend to give them all the blame.

This volume is dedicated to all those brave men and women who have been forced off the land by the trend towards bigger farms and fewer people on them. I also want to recognise the efforts of the Breadwinner without which I would have been among them.

The story so far

CHARLIE ALLAN'S family have been farming in Aberdeenshire for at least three hundred years. On his mother's side an unbroken line of tenant farmers goes back to the eighteenth century at about which time, on his father's side, one great progenitor was hanged for sheep-stealing. Whether he was a farmer is not known but we may stretch a point and say that he was involved in agriculture.

In the early 1920s, the lairds of Aberdeen, who knew more about spending money than about making it, sold their farms on the north side of the Ythan and the author's grandfather was able to buy Little Ardo as sitting tenant, despite the fact that by that time he was in fact sitting at North Ythsie in the neighbouring parish of Tarves.

Charlie's father, the author, John R. Allan and his mother, the educationist and poet Jean Mackie, bought the place in 1945 and sold it to the author at a handsome profit in 1976.

A period of rapid expansion into pedigree cattle, new sheds and overdrafts was undertaken until, in the early eighties, each acre of Little Ardo was burdened with £1,000 of debt.

By taking a job with the BBC, by selling six of the seven hundred cattle and by merciless exploitation of his wife (The Breadwinner) the situation was retrieved and by 1986 it was felt that the author had earned a rest. The Breadwinner took him off for three years in Kenya while she operated computers for the government and earned each day enough bread for both of them.

They returned to Little Ardo in the spring of 1989. Charlie would farm the acres his ancestors had made fertile and, though it was certainly her turn for a rest, and just in case, the Breadwinner would work in the toon.

That was the starting point for this Diary.

Volume One covered the return to Scotland and the first attempts to make profits grow where none had grown before. The stock were rebuilt, the digger and the new old tractor were bought and a new set of acquaintances met. Envy of the Red Rooster, Crookie and Mossie, the big farmers, inched towards fever pitch.

Volume Two saw the mad scheme to implant beef

5

embryos in Jerseys cows come to its expected conclusion. Pigs were introduced and more lessons learned. Not much is learned at the discussion group that meets on Sundays at the Salmon Inn but at least there is the odd laugh with Gowkie the sma hudder, my neighbours Hillie and Mains, Big Hamish who is a member of the 1000 acre club but has somehow retained his innocence, and Potions the chemist who comes to play at farmers and ends up with half the work to do.

Volume Three covers the period from March 1992 to June 1993. Mossie has come on for agricultural adviser (Honorary). He has employed a new contractor and taken on the role of chemist himself. But all is still not well. For this is the age of the administrative muddle. The Farmer now needs passports for his cattle, he needs to fill up the dreaded and mysterious IACS forms to collect his pensions from the government, and the hallowed ground of his forefathers has to be turned over to weeds....it is the age of set-aside.

The Breadwinner is still winning bread in the toon. The two Investments are still in work and showing a splendid return on their education. The older Wasting Asset has at last perceived the connection between the earning of money and the spending of it. He still spends more money than the Farmer ever dreamed of but at least the boy is now earning it. He has succeeded in getting a Breadwinner of his own and between them they run a good greasy spoon in the Broch. He is now known as the Recovery Stock.

That leaves only one Wasting Asset. He rents a cottar house on the farm and so is available, at carefully chosen times of day, for herding, holding paling posts and other jobs the farmer cannot manage on his own.

As Volume Three opens there are still only three grandchildren (all Investments) but there is a gleam in the Recovery Stock's eye. As I write there are four new generation Investments and the gleam is back in the Recovery Stock's eye.

Goodbye to two old friends

I SAID goodbye to two old friends this week. It was sad to see them go but it is the nature of this hard industry and the hard times we are going through. There was a time when we could have held on to them for old times sake. We could have given them a retirement, put them out to grass. But with profit hard to come by and MacSharry on the horizon as well as in the woodpile we just can't afford any fat about the place.

First to go was the post-hole borer. It had been my pride and joy when I bought it at the Highland Show in 1989. All my life I had gone to shows to look at all the stuff I would be able to buy when it was ten years old. But here I had bought a brand new "Arrow" post-hole borer with the paint hardly dry. I looked forward to covering Little Ardo with new fences which I would put up without breaking sweat.

And sweat is what we had needed up till now for Little Ardo is a stony devil of a place. We have eight inches of good second class land then a pan which is as hard as rotten rock and full of rock that is far from rotten. And the great James Low who was grieve here for forty six years and set the standards had decreed that a strainer hole had to be deep enough to bury a whole spade. I modified that to "the whole spade less the handle" but even so it was back breaking work.

It was with the greatest of pride, therefore, that I yoked the shiny new post-hole borer. I needed a fence round the silage bales. Normally that would have been two wires teetering on a few posts with stays at the corners but with the post-hole borer I would put up a Rolls-Royce. I made sure the contractor and all his men were there to see.

The post-hole borer chewed through the black earth like a knife through butter but she started to chew shear bolts as soon as she hit our stony pan. I remember thinking it was just like the banker... no damned use when you need him. As long

as you've plenty money the banker can't lend you enough. But as soon as you get in trouble the banker is first in the queue wanting his money back. The post-hole borer made light work of the easy bit but when there was work to do we just had to yoke the spade anyway.

Farmers will recognise that that was not a total disaster. We buy equipment for two basic reasons and helping with the work is only one of them. Even though it proved unfit for work the post-hole borer was still available for impressing the neighbours and the staff. I left it in the open sided shed that looks out into the close so that it could be admired by everyone who came about the place. And as to the staff; well, there's only me and I was impressed.

Nevertheless the post-hole borer has had to go. With the disaster we made of last year's harvest we couldn't admire her any longer so, when a contractor came and offered me almost sixty per cent of what I had paid for her, we could afford to covet her no longer.

Then there was old Johnder the bull. He was coming over his own stock and his replacement had been bought, so, on Friday, he had to go too.

Johnder had really been the opposite of the post-hole borer. He had not been much admired by the neighbours. Indeed, I had hidden him for

8

the visit of one of my pals from the old days of pedigree breeding, and he did nothing for the morale of the staff. On the other hand Johnder could fairly serve cows. He was a bit unromantic. If you put him in beside a cow in season it was up and at her without even going round the front to say, "good morning". But he fairly put them in calf.

And I've had more evidence this spring of the success of Johnder's approach. Last year I had ten or so heifers to go to the bull so I would get a hire of a Belgian Blue to look after them. Simmentals have a reputation for big calves and these were small Black Herefords or Jersey crosses. I made sure the heifers were well fed in a separate park for the arrival of the Belgian. He was with us for three weeks and yet we only saw him working a couple of times. We thought he must be a quiet worker but now we know different. The first of his calves are due in three weeks time and yet four of the heifers have calved.

Oh, yes. Johnder had clearly got wind of my lack of faith and taken matters into his own hands and our fences are not an insuperable obstacle to an enthusiastic bull.

Good old boy. They may be his grandchildren as well as his children but they are fine big calves without being too big.

Johnder fairly let us know that he wasn't happy when the new bull came home from Perth. He roared and pawed the ground and became quite threatening towards me. Little Ardo obviously wasn't big enough for the three of us.

He had always been the most amenable of bulls but I worried about how we would get Johnder into the float. In the end it was easy. We had an old Jersey cow going to the jingo-ring the same day so we put her in first. When Johnder saw her, his enthusiasm for his work got the better of him and he scrambled enthusiastically up the tail-door and away to oblivion. Even in the land of bulls, a bony old Jersey cow is probably not the ideal travelling companion, but he seemed to think it was a good way to go.

Johnder did better than the post-hole borer. In the jingo-ring he made 92.8 per cent of what I paid for him and he left me some fine calves. He is still leaving me calves; there was one born the day after Johnder left.

Black bull brings back memories

THERE'S A Black bull come home to Little Ardo for the first time for thirty years. I bought it at Thainstone at last week's Spring Show and it has caused a good deal of head-shaking and self-satisfied reminders that "I told you so."

You see I was one of those who in the late sixties and seventies imported Charolais, Simmentals, Chianinas and "other reptiles" as one of my neighbours called them. We were widely accused of ruining the British beef industry. Perhaps we did for there is damned little profit at it for all the success of the continental cattle and certainly there are those who are saying that I've seen sense at last in buying an Aberdeen Angus Bull.

In fact I have considered keeping a Black bull right from the start to give the heifers a small calf to start with. I couldn't bear to do it in the early days with black calves worth a hundred pounds and the pure continentals worth five thousand. But now that the difference at birth is only something like fifty per cent it seems worth it. Heifers who get an easy start are more likely to have a live calf and more likely to return quickly to the bull... they don't know they're getting the big bull second time round.

And this year I have fifty heifers to bull on the first of June.

You will remember that last April I bought thirty Black Hereford calves for fifty pounds a piece. Well they will be fourteen months old in June and should be just right for the bull. Or at least they should be but they look awfully small. Hence the new bull... and I'm going to give him a pure Simmental heifer as well, mostly out of curiosity.

The last Black bull at Little Ardo was also here to give the heifers an easy calving. In those days my father had a dairy and Auld Dodd, as he was called with pride but not affection, looked after the cows well enough but he threw far too big a calf for

the heifers. We had a tough time calving them with dead calves, heifers put off milking and subsequent infertility.

So for two hundred pounds my father bought Blackie whose legs were so short they only just reached the ground. He could almost pass underneath the old bull without bending down but he seemed to have a way with the heifers. They popped out small calves that bounced up and sucked right away. And the two hundred pounds was soon returned because of the better prices we got for the black calves. Auld Dodd's bull calves made about thirty shillings whereas the black

bull calves could sell for as much as twenty pounds if they were out of a good big cow.

And they all were out of a big strong cow. James Low the grieve made sure of that. In fact they were all out of the same cow. If he asked to see the calf's mother, the buyer would be taken into the byre and shown the huge beefy Blue cow whose name I have forgotten but who stood in the corner of the byre nearest to the dairy and gave up to seven gallons of milk a day.

All of that came back to me as I tied up my new Black bull in the byre on Wednesday night. I remembered, with some shame, that my own breeding record had not been that good.

Like the Charolais bull I have a rather large head. I got it from my father and I am not altogether displeased with it. I have always taken comfort in the old saying; "Big head and little wit, never gaed thegither yet". But I have to admit that it is not an asset in reproduction.

Our first child had my father's big head and my poor wife struggled for two days before they finally delivered her with a high forceps. I remember going in to see Fiona as if it were yesterday. She was half sat up in bed looking exhausted but very beautiful. She was in some pain but had the pride of achievement and the gallant desire not to double her discomfort by sharing it.

She was eager to know if I had seen the baby. I had indeed. She was at the Benneton stage and on the way to the incubator. I was shown a little bloody punched up face all scratch marks from the tongs. I told Fiona our daughter was beautiful, as she subsequently became.

She smiled at me and with only a hint of reproach said, "You're lucky you're not a bull. If you had been you'd have been down the road as soon as I could get a bit of beef on you."

Over the years she managed that but spared me the jingo-ring. Luckily you are only a heifer once and though the heads didn't get any smaller the births became easier until at the fourth confinement she only just made it to the theatre in time.

Still, Fiona, showing a remarkable grasp of the farming ethos, is happy to see a Black bull home at Little Ardo. She is not very anthropomorphic but whenever we had a hard calving she didn't like it.

When the new bull came home I took him round to see the other half of the partnership. She cast the farmer's eye over him and said, "Aye your heifers are lucky. I should have got the Black bull for an easy start."

I thought there was a faraway look in her eye. But I wasn't sure.

Worrying myself on the beach

BY THE time you are reading this I will be sunning myself on a beach in the Canary Islands. I didn't want to go of course, there is plenty to do here and there'll be very little profit in a trip to the sun. But The Breadwinner must have a winter break so she bought the tickets. In those circumstances what could The Farmer do but go?

It's hardly an ideal time. My heifers which were reserved for the Belgian Blue bull should be calving, if there are any left. So far old Johnder has accounted for five, snaffled from under our very noses by what must have been some very dainty dyke jumping. Then the barley will need its spring spray as there is just a hint of mildew starting....it could be rampant by the time we get back.

Of course the farm is not going to be left entirely to itself. The youngest Wasting Asset is at home between fortunes and recovering from his latest broken leg. He is actually a very able fencer (and I'm not talking swords here) so I'm hoping to return to a race of new Belgian calves, all the rest of the stock fit and well and the spring fencing all done.

It could happen that way of course but I fear the worst.

You see, Newton, a new member of our discussion group, left a neighbour with grand ideas in charge when he went on holiday three years ago. At that time his work-horse was a somewhat disreputable looking digger first registered in 1970. When Newton returned from his break his friend met him with the news that he wasn't going to be driving that old wreck and that he had bought him a new one. It cost him £13,000 to change.

Now what worries me is not just that the Wasting Asset has champagne tastes to go with his Irn Bru income, but that he thinks I'm a millionaire. And worse than that is the fact that Potions (the local chemist who likes to come down to the farm to play) has also offered a watching brief. He is the sort

13

who has a ten thousand pound car and no understanding of the economics of modern agriculture.

But worst of all is that my new honorary crop consultant will be about the place while I am away. Mossie believes that I make a fundamental mistake in my farming. He thinks my gates tied up with string, pens made out of wired-together pallets and scrap machinery is all wrong.

"You've got to have everything NIIICE," he says. If it's nae NIIICE you'll just get fed up o't, you winna pay attention and it'll be a DISAAASTER." He's right, I know. And I am getting things redd up. I have just paid eight hundred pounds to the blacksmith for fine new doors and feeders for the pigs. But I've tried farming with an overdraft of a thousand pounds an acre and I don't want to pass that way again.

So you see the thought of what those three millionaires are going to do with my money when I'm away may well wreck my holiday.

I am reminded of Wattie, the crofter from these parts, who would take his wife to London to see the sights at the time of the great Smithfield Show. They had never had a holiday south of Stonehaven so it was a major step. All was set though and the couple were agog with a mixture of fear and excitement when, on the very eve of their departure, Daisy the house cow had gone down with milk fever.

Well, that was it. There could be no Smithfield that year.

The plan had been to leave the farm in the tender charge of a fifteen year old loon the couple had just employed to ease the burdens of their advancing years. It had seemed a bold enough plan to leave a fifteen year old in charge of the croft when all was well. But with Daisy down and the vet called the trip would have to be called off.

And yet the loon was such a cheery and optimistic fellow. That was what they had liked most about him when he had come for his interview; there was nothing he wouldn't do and he was so cheery. "Na, na," said the loon. "I'll easy manage. Awa ye go and enjoy yersels. My father once had four coos wi' milk fever and I cured the lot, nae bother."

The tickets being already paid and not subject to refunds, Wattie agreed, against his better judgement, to go to London. Off he went leaving the loon with every imagin-

14

able instruction for the comfort and curing of Daisy.

Wattie spent the most miserable four days of his life trailing round Madame Tussauds, the Tower of London, Hyde Park Corner, and Buckingham Palace. He could hardly see the Changing of The Guard he was so worried about Daisy. And the wife couldn't see it either for she was too small.

Beldie was quite out of her depth in London anyway so it didn't matter that she didn't see the guards. The only sign she showed of interest was when they were on a bus tour. The guide was droning on about the Houses of Parliament and Big Ben when a cat ran across the road. Beldie sat up and asked "And wha's cattie's that?"

When, at last they won home Wattie was sick with anticipation about his cow. They were met by the loon in the close. He was cheery and confident as ever.

"How did ye enjoy the Show?"

"Grand. How did you get on?"

"Oh, it went like clockwork. It was nae bother tae me," said the loon cheerily.

"And how's Daisy?"

"Oh, aye, she's dead," said the loon, cheerily.

When I think of that loon I think of my return from the sun. I am met by my three guardians. Mossie speaks first, "It was a pity about the calves but we saved maist o'

15

the heifers. And we thocht we'd better mak a start to takin doon the auld steadin because you'd never dae it. Once we'd made a start the rest jist fell doon. And we'd never have managed if we hadna done something about the auld digger. It was only thirteen thousand to change."

Out of my depth in Lake Ardo

THE FARMER and The Breadwinner have won home from Tenerife and none of the disasters that I feared has come to pass. The younger Wasting Asset and Potions, overseen by Mossie (there would have been no hope of keeping him out anyway) have handled all with aplomb. No deaths at all. Only one calfie born but "both doing fine". Not only that but the silage grass has all been re-fenced and the cows excluded from it, and the whole thing neater and tidier than I left it.

And there have been improvements. Up till now bringing cattle up from the lower fields has meant getting the digger to block the close off. With the bucket and the back-acter down it makes a fine mobile and flexible gate but it is a bit of a scutter.

But when the farmer returned from his holidays there were two gleaming new strainers in, one at either side of the close and two brand new gates that can swing each way without grounding. Mossie says that is NIIICE!

It would not be like me to be pleased altogether of course, and I'm not. These two new gates are hung on expensive looking split new and painted smiddy-made strainers. I wouldn't mind quite so much if it were not for the fact that, as near as they could be to the new gates without getting in the way, I keep a stack of perfectly good strainers made out of second hand telephone poles.

And they needn't think I don't know what the game is. The next generation knows I won't go on for ever and they want every improvement to be as NIIICE as possible while I'm still paying for it.

And what of the holiday?

Well, we went to Los Gigantes which is a little sun-soaked tourist trap on the South side of the island. The phone didn't ring, no bills came in and no cattle broke out so it couldn't fail to be a good holiday.

We were ripped off in the usual ways... when we asked

17

what Polynesian dishes they served at the candle-lit Polynesian Restaurant we were met by a most accomplished "Me no speaka da Engleesh" routine. The romance of the place was further reduced when Fiona discovered that the candle was in fact a little candle-shaped gas canister. Still we stayed and had the most expensive meal of the trip.

We were told that we were lucky because it was Carnival time in Los Gigantes.

You may have heard of a similar event called the Mardi Gras which they hold each year in Brazil. I haven't been to that one but, though I'm told it is bigger, I don't see how it could be noisier.

There was a delightful parade of dancers and bands (like an orange or green parade without the seriousness of purpose). The costumes were wonderful and the rhythms really exciting. There was a fireworks display and the ceremonial roasting and eventual drowning of a giant sardine. Apart from that there was dancing and concerts in the little village square until four o'clock in the morning.

The whole thing would have been a joy in the days before electronic amplification. But the sound system at Los Gigantes would have done for the biggest outdoor rock festival in the world and our balcony looked right into the square.

We left our hotel and took an apartment down by the harbour for the last three days of Carnival. We were so busy making up our sleep that we missed a lot of the fun.

The only disaster of the holiday occurred when I was leaving. On my rounds I noticed that the calf I had half-noticed the day before, really did have a touch of pneumonia and really did need a jab. As I was taking the Wasting Asset round to go over his duties I thought we would give it its first jab there and then.

I primed the syringe and handed it to the lad. Then with the stealth of an Apache after revenge, I snuck up behind the calf and grabbed its tail.

Now there is a part of the midden at Little Ardo which unkind visitors have referred to as Lake Ardo on account of the fact that with the best will in the world there can never be less than three inches of slurry in it. With excitement of the impending holiday the best will in the world had not prevailed and Lake Ardo would have been at a depth of seven or eight inches.

There was a time when I

could have held onto the tail of a three month old calf with one hand and lit my pipe with other. That day has gone, which would not be so dangerous if I didn't still imagine I had the strength that once threw the hammer and tossed the caber.

Instead of letting go when the calf set off, I held on with both hands and all my remaining might. Caught by surprise, I was jerked forward and off balance. The only hope was to run faster than the calf and regain equilibrium but I could not. My arms were pulled further and further forward so that to retain a footing I had to stretch my legs further and further with every step.

Finally there was a horrendous tearing of ham-strings and my right leg gave way. I crumpled forward and, cracking my arthritic knee on the bottom, landed flat in Lake Ardo.

The pain was excruciating for a couple of minutes, great for a bit longer and hard to conceal from the Bread-winner for a few days. It's still not nearly right, but you know, as the first stabs of pain started to subside, as I looked up from my bath of sh... you know what, as I saw the Wasting Asset looking remarkably concerned, all I could think was "what a pity we hadn't had a home video going. We would surely have won a prize from Jeremy Beedle or his execrable imitators on the BBC."

The Wasting Asset told me that, as he was wondering

19

if it would be safe to laugh, he too was thinking the spectacle was worthy of a wider audience.

Surely farming has not come to this; a series of game-show opportunities interspersed by dismal trips to the bank.

Beef job doesn't fool Mossie

OUR NEW Simmental bull has been having a hard time of it. He keeps getting his head stuck in the angle barriers through which he has to eat his silage. The Aberdeen Angus is all right. His neat head pops in and out without touching the sides but the Simmie is just the wrong size.

If he had been bigger, like Johnder the old bull he replaced, he would have had to eat over the top of the barrier. Sometimes he does but on three occasions he has pushed so hard against it that he has stuck. The extraordinary thing is that he doesn't get his head right in. He gets stuck at the boney bump above his eyes.

Three times now I have had to go for the hacksaw and saw through the thick box steel while Argus (as he is cried) shows the patience of Job. It is a slow business and one decidedly not to my liking. Apart from the times my hand gets crushed between boney head and cold steel there is the sad fact that I am rapidly demolishing my feed barrier. There are now three missing spars which provide convenient popholes for calves to get out and tramp about among the feed.

So this suggests another criterion in buying bulls. When I need a new one in two years time I'll be looking for one with a really big head.

Many people I know will say that that is crazy because of the calving difficulties a big head can cause but I find that the calving problems caused by a big head are all to the good. The point is that if a cow has difficulty in producing the calf's head you have maybe twelve hours to do something about it. But if the calf has a little head which pops out and the calf then sticks at the heart you have only a few minutes to save it.

Anyway, Argus has got quite a reputation to live up to, for old Johnder's last crop of calves have got off to a flying start. We have seven good calves and we still have not got to the alleged calving date. It took more than a mere fence to keep old Johnder

from his work. Not only that but five of the calves were from heifers and only two were seen calving.

At the other end of the beef job the situation is pretty bleak. We've had years of constant prices which won't do in this inflationary world. I was speaking to John Macintosh, who has been butchering in the North East for many years. He told me he thought the beef job had just about had it, though he used a turn of phrase more suitable for casual conversation than for printing in the *Herald*.

That was an alarming assessment from a man who has always seemed to get a living when we farmers were finding it hard. In the days when we used to get a subsidy which went up when the price went down and vice versa I once told John that I was afraid that the subsidy wasn't big enough. "Well, Charlie," said John Macintosh, "I'm doin' my best for you there." Certainly he never seems to pay more than he has to.

I had been selling four fat beasts at the new centre at Thainstone. As always happens when you are selling, the job didn't seem to me to be quite so bad.

The two heifers were home grown. They were twenty-two months old and their mothers had only cost £220 plus a year's keep when they were bulled. The two averaged £499 and, with nearly £100 of subby on the cows, I can't think but that that left me something.

The stots on the other hand averaged £742. They had been bought, by my agent Sandy Fowlie, in a batch which averaged £490 eleven months ago. The rise of £252 looks good until you start to count it up.

Interest on the buying bill comes to about £65. Half an acre of grass and manure thereon comes to £60. They ate more than a tonne of barley each, say £130. That is a loss already and I haven't said anything about the ad-lib silage, straw, minerals, worming(twice), transport from Dingwall and to Inverurie. And naturally there is nothing in this for labour... but then there never is.

My grain baron and pig-farming neighbour, Mossie, has known the truth about the beef trade for many years but has had the greatest difficulty with his son. Russel was desperate to have stotties which he was sure would be better than those stinking pigs.

Mossie taught him the truth in the best possible way. He bought 90 stotties last backend and prepared them for the Christmas market. They did well, they were sold at a good price (208 pence a kilo clean-in) and the financial outcome was far above average. In fact if one hadn't died he would have broken even.

Mossie showed his son the balance sheet. "Now Russel. See that? That's your stotties for you. Jist a disaster."

He didn't like making a loss but he reckons the lesson will be cheap in the long run and save Russel from losing a fortune over the years.

He's trying to get me to stop the fattening of cattle too. He tells me that I can plough up all my grass and sow linseed. He thinks the seeds I grow will almost pay for the growing of the crop and that Mr MacSharry will give me £230 an acre of a subsidy. He can't understand why I am hesitating... and neither can I.

Rich odour of pork on the trotter

ABOUT THIS uncertain industry, in this uncertain world, I am in the position to make one confident prediction. The price of pigs, which has risen from 83 pence to 123 pence a kilo in a few short months, has peaked and is about to fall. You see I have at last managed to get my hands on a small batch.

In our last session of discussing the ills of the world and the hazards of our profession before I went off on holiday, Mossie and I agreed that the Average All Pigs Price was now too high and that pigs should no longer be bought.

Imagine my surprise therefore, on returning from my ten days in the sun, when I caught the unmistakable smell of pork on the trotter.

"What the hell's this, Moss?" said I with all the restraint I could muster. "I thought we had agreed they were too dear to buy now?"

"Oh, aye. We didna scutter aboot. As soon as you were on the plane it was "action". Some difference frae you ditherin while the price rose and rose again."

There was no use arguing but if the price falls as much in the next ten weeks as it rose in the last ten I will lose all the small margins I made on my last three batches of weaners. And I confidently anticipate just such a fall. That is just what happens to me. If I need rain for the neeps all I have to do is to cut some hay.

But with the miracles of modern financial markets there is a way in which I can avoid this dire prospect. I can sell my piggies on the futures markets. They cost about thirty-seven pounds each and they will cost me about thirty pounds to feed. So at 68 kilos deadweight I need about 99 pence a kilo to break even.

Now it seems altogether likely that the price will be below a pound by the end of May when mine are fat, but the market does not agree. As I write, I could sell on the futures market at no fewer than 123.9 pence a kilo. That is surely too good to be true

24

because, if the piggies live and convert average well, that should give me nearly seventeen pounds a pig to pay the costs of dealing and compensate for last year's bad harvest.

I find the whole deal hard to believe. You see I am not selling to a butcher for delivery in May. No pigs will ever change hands on that futures market... it is all just a financial gamble.

The deal is based on the last Average All Pigs Price in May. I am gambling that it will be less than 123.9 pence and someone else is betting that it will be more. So, if the last AAP is 100 pence, the other gambler will have to give me 23.9 pence a pig and I will get 100 pence from the abattoir. If, on the other hand, the last AAP in May is 150 pence I will have to shell out 26.1 pence but the slaughterhouse will pay 150 pence for my piggies.

Either way I get 123.9 pence which would be very acceptable and about three times the surplus I have ever had before.

In theory.

But what happens if my piggies finish long before the end of May or well into June? I could settle my futures contract at 150 pence a kilo but only get 110 at the abattoir. That would be a disaster.

And there are other snags.

You have to deposit £2000 pounds at 8.5 % interest in order to deal on the market and what happens if the traders go bust? Why should they be any different?

Anyway we have grave doubts about exactly how the system works, if at all. The only way we're going to find out is to try it so my £2000 is away to London.

Mind you, Mossie is true to form. Having justified his expensive purchase on my behalf by pointing out the possibility of selling on the futures… having caused me to part with my two grand … he is screaming at me not to sell on the grounds that the price of pigs is heading for the ceiling.

I can't sell anyway until my £2000 has been processed but in the meantime I have made a remarkable discovery which should help my piggies' conversion rate.

You will remember that my last lot converted at above three pounds of meal to one pound of pork. It was the first time I'd been that high and I was disappointed. Well now, I have a Shorthorn cross Ayrshire cow which has come through the winter quite extra-ordinarily well and I have discovered why.

At the back of the piggery where we keep our pig feed bin is the door out and in through which the cows have gone all winter. I am not often round there but on Saturday I was and there I saw the cross Ayrshire licking at the concrete below the bin.

There was clearly a leak in the flexible auger which automatically conveys the feed into the shed. I presumed that there would be a spillage of dust when the auger was on and smiled at the old girl's resourcefulness.

But when I saw just how resourceful she was being the smile was quickly wiped off my face. Having licked the platter clean she then gave the pipe a sharp butt with the top of her nose and caused a shower of pig nuts to spill out from the joint of the pipe and the bin.

How long she has been at that I don't know, nor do I know if she has been doing it for the rest of the cows but she'll not do it again for I've got the pipe fenced off. However the futures works out that is bound to help my performance on the physical pork market.

26

April 13, 1992

New status for Rastus the bull

IT HAS been a good week for our new Aberdeen Angus bull. You will recall that I bought him to look after thirty Black Hereford heifers the best of which I hope to add to my suckler herd. That had been a big surprise to all my neighbours. They were astonished that I, who was in on the ground floor with seven of the European breeds that came flooding in in the seventies, should go back to the most traditional, the most British breed of all.

Well, I wanted easy calvings and I knew that the Aberdeen Angus was likely to give me that despite the Holstein influence that has been brought in from Canada.

Mind you last year I hired a Belgian Blue bull because, as well as nicking very well with the few Jerseys I have left, the Blues are recommended by some for heifers. Everyone knows that they are the worst cattle in the world for calving in the pure and that as many as half have to be born by caesarean section, but the huge hips that get in the way in the pures are supposed to be absent at birth in the crosses.

I won't say I was convinced but, there being no doubt that the Belgians are top of the market when they are fat, it seemed worth a try.

I know now, for we had three calvings this week. I know it doesn't mean all calves will be like it but these were exactly the wrong shape for calving, in my opinion. They had small heads which popped out as soon as the heifers started calving. The bodies were a struggle and then they all three stuck at the hurdies. I would much rather a big head which would be too big to come out until the cow was fully dilated. As soon as the head comes out I want the rest to come easily. If it sticks at the head you can have a day to do something about it. If it sticks at the navel you may have a couple of minutes and as I discovered with the first of my heifers this week you may have as much as an hour if it sticks at the hurdies.

27

I found her lying most uncomfortably half though the fence and into the wood at the bottom of the field. As I approached I could hear the calf baaing so I was happy that at least I had a live calf. It would only be a question of disentangling the cow and all would be well.

But, to my horror, I discovered that the calf was quite stuck at the hurdies and was still half inside its mother. It was roaring loud and strong and trying to scramble clear with its front legs but was quite stuck. I had calving ropes with me but only succeeded in pulling the pair down into the wood.

Up to the farm I went for the Wasting Asset (who was still asleep) and the American calf puller. The calf was still baaing when we returned but we couldn't get it out even with the calf puller. I eventually managed to turn it with a pinch bar and with a crack the calf won clear. It had taken an hour and I have never seen a calf out like that for that amount of time and it live.

And I'm afraid I still haven't. It was breathing strongly but I could get no movement out of the back legs. It held its head up but I didn't like the look of my calf. I took my jacket off to cover it from the wind and rain and set off for the vet while the Wasting Asset set off to the village for four hot water bottles. The vet came but his injections, the hot water bottles nor my jacket were enough to save it. It's temperature was down to 94 and we never got it up again. While half of it had been inside its mother the calf was kept warm but after it got out it cooled quickly. My first Belgian Blue cross calf lived for two and a half hours.

We did better with the next two, but the outlines were the same. As soon as the water was off the head was there. That was easy to get out. The body was a stiff job with an anxious moment at the chest and then they both stuck at the hips. We got them though, and I have two beautiful calves which will one day be worth eight hundred pounds each.

However it is all good news for Rastus the black bull. He only cost £840 and might easily have found himself back on the beef market if the Belgian Blue calvings had been all the we'd been anticipating. Now he can look forward to the happiest month of June a young bull could hope for. And I hope he gets the weather for it.

I don't know how intelligent Rastus is but he may re-

alise that it is not just the certainty of his position that has looked up this week. The whole status of the job in hand has been elevated. His calves will not just be any-old calves they will be FASL calves.

That's the Farm Assured Scotch Livestock scheme which we are getting off the ground to show consumers that our meat is consumer friendly, ozone friendly and animal friendly. We were inspected this week and, knowing that the scheme's architect Maitland Mackie had failed the initial inspection, I feared the worst. Mossie was delighted at the prospect, "Oh! You'll get a scolding," he said.

But I needn't have worried. The inspector didn't like my medicine records much, and he wants me to keep better records of non-pedigree cattle's pedigrees. I signed the undertaking to do those things and got onto Mossie at once.

"Mossside? Yes? This is the ARDO QUALITY ASSURED LIVESTOCK here."

That fairly put his gas at a peep.

Mossie's a subsidy junkie

THERE HAVE been two developments this week at the little farm on Ardo's hill. Both are things of beauty, but whereas one may well be a joy forever and will certainly see my time out, the other is an abominable insult to the brave men and women who broke the land in from the moss.

I have started a new drystane dyke. It's the latest move to keep the Breadwinner not just winning bread, but sharing it with me. I have told you that she doesn't find that the midden and the heaps of silage bales enhance her lifestyle here on the farm. But, despite the fact that she is a banker's daughter and born to more refined things, she does understand that those are necessary evils on a stock farm.

But for all our thirty-odd years together I have failed to convince her of the necessity of the dubbs in the close, the plastic bags and bale netting all over the place, nor for the scrap heap which used to adorn the very heart of the farm. Well the scrap heap is all gone now on Big Hamish's seventeen tonne skip. The grass seeds are bought and so is the ride-on mower.

And now I have started the piece de resistance. I have started to build a drystane dyke at the back of the rubbish dump which is to be a lawn. It needs something there to stop the cattle getting into the wood. The easy thing would have been barbed wire. We already have some post and rail fencing but I didn't want the place looking like Newmarket or altogether like a hobby farm. So it had to be drystanes.

There are about ten miles of drystane dykes put round this place by the first two generations of us here. It is the traditional material and the dykes look right.

Or they did. So many of them are now falling down and, of course, it is just too big a job to build them up again. It used to be done in my father's time when there were six men here looking for a job half the year. But now

30

when there is only me and the occasional visitor like the Wasting Asset or Potions the chemist who comes to play at farmies, the dykes are mostly falling slowly down. I have a vague intention to double fence them to stop the cattle knocking them so badly but ten miles of fencing would be necessary to do the job and that is a lot of money.

Anyway, I've made a start to a new wall at the steading and it is looking well. We are gathering stones off the spring rape ground just now and I put all the good building stones off beside my wall before dumping the rest as metal for the new road round to the pig-feed bin. That way I feel I am getting on with three jobs at once and that is a good feeling.

I have twelve of the eighty feet of my dyke built and it is looking well, though I'm not too keen on anybody leaning on it. I think my ancestors will be looking up at me and nodding their approval. And I anticipate joining them and looking up at future generations and enjoying a little joke at their expense.

You see, when I was modifying the old barn to make it easier to muck by tractor, I discovered a stone with "1857" neatly engraved on it. It had been put there by William Yull when he built the barn in The Golden Age of Agriculture. I intend to build that stone into my new dyke. That will fairly fox them.

The dyke is all good news. But there is bad news too.

And almost inevitably, I suppose, Mossie is to blame. He has been so demoralised by the lunacy of the Common Agricultural Policy that, from having been the most skilful barley baron of them all, he is now just a subsidy junkie. He has gone daft for the daftest of all Euro madness ...linseed oil.

He has bullied the Red Rooster into growing linseed on some of his priceless Less Favoured Area hill. Can you imagine it... a hundred pound a cow land and he's going to grow linseed on it? He cannot possibly grow more than say eighty pounds worth of linseed per acre unless there is a huge upsurge in cricket playing in Scotland leading to a shortage for oiling the bats. And it is much more likely that the Rooster will end up baling the stuff and dumping it in a quarry as Mossie himself did some years ago.

But of course that is not the point. The point is that the madmen of Europe are offering us about £240 an acre in subsidy just to sow the stuff. Some attempt has to be made to harvest it, of course, but even at that he can hardly lose.

Worse than that, Mossie has bullied me into growing some too. Mind you, I am too scared of what my ancestors would say about that to do it at Little Ardo, but there is a fine old widow body in the village who lets me twenty acres of the oldest grass you have ever seen. I'm just away to tell her that the government wants to give me five thousand pounds to grow blue flowers on her land. If it is O.K. with her I am going into subsidy farming in a big way.

I'd rather be producing food.

Mossie's pigs do the trick

MOSSIE HAS another success on his hands. As well as his 200 sows, the grain Baron has a loose housed unit where he can fatten 800 weaners at a time. Taking one lot with another, those should leave him around £5 a pig.

For anyone else in the world that fiver would be made up to £15 this time, and a loss of £5 the next. But Mossie, to the fury of the rest of us, seems to manage so to time things that he misses out of the losses and only gets the good batches.

It is hard to believe that there is somebody up there who loves him, but there is evidence to that effect. Certainly, he has a batch going fat at the moment - and they are leaving him about £23 a pig. That is a contribution to overheads of over £18,000. Even though his overheads - incurred largely in the best watering holes in the district - are considerable, it does help to keep our man cheerier in these difficult times.

He phoned me up on his mobile the day after the election. He had been depressed when he woke that forenoon, so he had gone up to his outfarm to look at the speculative pigs, and it had fairly done the trick. "I'm just sittin on a bale and lookin at profit on the hoof. I'm just on a high. In fact, I'll need to get some stronger shear bolts so that the baler can cope with all the money I'm makin."

Now it so happened that I had the teletext on, and was watching the shares bounding upward in celebration of Mr Major's win. The Breadwinner has a few shares, and I know what they are - so, despite the fact that I am old enough to remember that Labour has been much better for farmers since the war, I was able to join Mossie on his high.

"Oh, there's the index up another point."

"There's a muckle piggie just gone up to the feeder. I must have a profit of £26 on it. Oh! I'm on a high."

Of course, I've got my 300-odd speculative pigs myself, but I have never got above £6 a head of profit. I expect the price of pigs will dive the week after next because Mossie's will all be away and mine will just be starting to go for bacon. Mind you, I won't lose the lot this time.

You see, I have sold 100 on the futures market and so locked myself into a price of 125p a kg. If you believe the market's publicity, that should give me a gross margin of some £14 a pig which, while it would be Mossie's worst ever, would be my best.

We'll see how this forward selling works out, but I must say that I think it is likely to be a mistake. The futures market is a pure gamble. No pigs ever change hands. So, if a lot of farmers sell on the futures and a lot of butchers buy on the futures, you would think that the losses would equal the gains.

And so it would, except that the market professionals - the speculators who have never seen a pig before it was bacon - have to be paid. And if you are going to out-guess them, you have to be up early.

I've tried it before in the days when I had potatoes, and my experience persuaded me that futures trading was bad for farmers. The theory was that as soon as you saw a reasonable price, rather than be greedy, you sold on the futures market,

The trouble was that in the bad years there tended not to be a reasonable price at all. And in the good years you always sold and thereby missed out on the bonanza you'd have got on the physical market.

And the point is that most years the potato lost money. What made growing them worthwhile was the klondyke you made every six years or so. Futures trading meant that the innocent farmer just sold as soon as he saw a decent price - and missed those klondykes.

It also seems I am to miss out on this year's linseed klondyke. My widow body is not going to let me plough up her old ley and sow the bonny blue flowers. "De ye think I cam' doon wi the last shoor o' rain," she said, rather discouragingly when I asked her. "Na, na. The parks'll nae be ploughed in my time."

I have great sympathy with her. Just because I am afraid of insulting my own ancestors by doing anything so daft at Little Ardo, is no good reason to inflict the insult on hers. She spotted that one right away. "Foo nae grow the stuff at hame?"

Still, the £5000 subsidy would have been handy.

34

Another man who won't be joining the ridiculous swing to linseed growing is Crookie. As a successful grain baron, he's the sort who should be growing the stuff if we're to have some decent crops. But he says he can't grow linseed because it is ready at the same time as the potato, and that is where most of his money comes from. Crookie is part of a group which has sold 1000 tonnes of Scottish seed to Russia. So it would be a good idea to make a job of the potato harvest.

But that is just an excuse. Firstly, the linseed harvest is so unlikely and of such pathetic value that there is no chance of it getting in the way of anything important. And second, the love that had all his pals buying eternity rings last Christmas has matured through proposal to acceptance and engagement. He gets married in October.

Chemical cocktail prescribed

I AM very happy to say that everything is going as well as could be expected. It even looks as though the farm might not be losing money just now. I'll tell you the reasons for my optimism in a minute but first I must tell you about one of our farming circle and the time he went to see the doctor.

I'm not normally shy about naming names but in these days of perpetual litigation I think discretion (and the fact that the doctor is involved) is the better part of cowardice.

Anyway the farmer has a big and hard-earned reputation as a boozer so it was something of a surprise when he went down to the doctor and said that he was baffled as to why he wasn't feeling well - nothing in particular just profoundly off-colour. No one of us who was in on his strange complaint had the slightest doubt as to the cause of the trouble.

Now it just so happens that the doctor, a much younger man is also acquiring a growing reputation for putting it away, so the two were well met.

The doctor gave our man a very thorough investigation, lasting about forty-five minutes and finally pronounced himself baffled. "Well I'm sorry. I've tried everything. I can't find a thing wrong. Maybe it's the drink."

"Oh, I see," said our man, "In that case, Doctor, I'll just come back when you're sober."

As you can imagine that story has given people hereabout a lot of happiness this week. It has added to the feeling that the general hopelessness of farming as a business accepted, the job is going well.

The spring rape is just peeping through the ground so no comment is possible there yet, except that it went in timeously to a dry bed. I was horrified to see the contractor rolling it eight days after sowing but it may not have been chitting yet as it had been cold.

The winter rape is looking first rate. It's just beginning to flower and is a complete contrast to last year's poor sparse affair. The wheat and the winter barley are looking special. Surely this is the year for the four tonne average - for both.

One reason for the improvement is undoubtedly the new regime for spraying. Last year I had my consultant who came and made recommendations. I then ordered the chemicals. Then the contractor came when he had finished everything else he had in his queue. That led often to horrendous delays. With the uncertain weather last spring and summer, the contractor was sometimes round making another recommendation before the previous job had been done.

Now that I have bought my own sprayer I can do the job right away. And having my own machine is especially good if the weather is dodgy. If the job is to be done by a contractor he has to be fairly sure that the weather will be fine all day for he doesn't want to risk getting stuck here watching the rain. With my own sprayer I can dodge the showers.

I was doing that this week and it was brought home to me just how important timing is. Mossie the Grain Baron, my honorary consultant, was screaming at me to "get that stuff on" the winter barley. It was all to do with the growth stage that the barley had reached.

Now this was all new to me. As far as I have always been concerned there had been six growth stages in the life of a cereal. First it chits. Then it breers (brairds). Then comes the flag leaf. It shoots. It (usually) lodges. And in growth stage six it ripens.

Imagine my astonishment therefore, to be told that it was vital to spray the barley at growth stage thirty-two. If there are as many stages as that then each stage can only last a few days. No wonder I have found the four tonne crop hard to grow up till now.

And then there is the variety and the sheer quantity of the stuff I had to put on. No fewer than nine chemicals were in the cocktail. In fact there was hardly room in the sprayer for the water.

Anyway on it went in good time, and in perfect conditions. It was a showery day, the sort which would have kept the contractor away, but I was able to dodge in and get it just right. The barley harvest is now bathed in expectation.

Even the beef enterprise is looking better just now. We have twenty-two calves, three-quarters bulls and only one loss. Even that is com-pensated for by a set of twins. And those calves are of a much higher standard than of recent years. You will recall that I was transplanting beef embryos into Jersey cows. That gave us good calves when it worked but in those for whom the implantation was a failure we were left with hopeless cross calves.

That's behind us now. The few remaining Jerseys are having Belgian Blue calves which are first rate and the other calves are all from beef cows.

But the star of the show this week is a Charolais stot. Big Ben was a grower and it looked as though we were going to have him forever, I first realised how big he was when he got in beside Johnder when the old boy was going off to market. He wasn't nearly as thick but he looked three inches taller than our stock bull.

Anyway Big Ben graded U4L and yielded 475 kilos of beef. That came to £1012 with the subby... the first time I have had over the ton for a commercial animal.

I know he had eaten a lot in his year at Little Ardo but surely the rise of £522 will have left a small margin.

38

May off to bad start

AYE, IT'S not all fun this farming. One moment you are carrying all before you and the next you are beset by so many little snags that you wonder what on earth you were feeling so good about.

May got off to a bad start. There are not many socialists among we farmers so I suppose it is quite appropriate that May Day should see a deterioration in my luck.

First there was the dead pig. That's to be expected any day if you've four hundred pigs but they were still all alive after seven weeks and I was thinking we had cracked it. And then again the death of a pig that is losing money isn't so bad but they are doing very well in the market just now. I got my first sixteen away last week and they averaged £87. A dead pig like that is a serious business.

But May Day had far worse in store. One of our last remaining Jerseys, who had a fine Belgian Blue bull calf a fortnight ago and had a slight paralysis of one of her back legs, went off her legs alto-gether. We now have to lift her up every day to let her stand for the calf and in the hope that she'll get mobile again. She's game but as soon as we have another cow for the calf I'm afraid she'll have to go.

And we'd trouble with another of the Jerseys. She'd been overdue to calve and I suspected a dead calf as she had stopped making a bag and opening up at the back. Anyway, two days before the end of April, I found her looking sad with afterbirth hanging from her and froth at her mouth. The vet was called immediately and to my astonishment and to the delight of the Wasting Asset who had looked in on the way home from a party, he produced a fine bull calf in the peak of condition.

I know the vet was pleased too. Even vets are human and it is such a nice change for them to be involved in a success. In the desperation to save money we nearly always call them too late. Anyway, he treated the

39

cow, came back and treated her the next day and on May Day my new calf was an orphan. She neither ate nor drank a thing after parturition.

And then there's the weather. The cattle which went outside with such joy and in such fine order are grazing with five mouths now. The grass should be growing away from them but instead, it is getting scarce and they are making things worse with every step they take. As I look out from my desk here I can see six cows and eight calves squelching round and round the Calfie's Park and turning it brown. If only they would stand still. The discussion group which meets at the Salmon Inn to chew the fat on a Sunday evening was giving the monsoon a go this week. The Red Rooster's having a hellova time trying to make ground on his hill for the ludicrous linseed. With the government going to pay us £240 an acre to make the country pretty with useless blue flowers he'll be hard to stop mind, but it was a bad year to start with. And Mossie is losing machinery at an alarming rate as he tries to get a linseed crop into the moss from which his farm gets its name.

But if we're depressed at our difficulties in exploiting the mania of MacSharry, Big Hamish is on a serious downer. First there was the matter of the silage bree that got into the river. It was hardly surprising with all the rain there'd been and we couldn't find it in our hearts to blame the big man... but the courts could.

He's been in hiding for weeks in fear of the penalty of two thousand pounds he would have imposed. But when the great day came they let him off with an order to get on and do whatever has to be done to make sure pollution won't happen again. That sounds all very well and you'd think he had got off lightly if I didn't tell you he has to spend £10,000 on new concrete. "I'd of been chepper wi a fine," he said sadly. So he would, of course, but the fish wouldn't.

Then there is the Spring work. The last time I spoke to him Hamish still had 100 acres of spring barley to sow. ·He's very good at sowing but his trouble is he sows all his neighbours' crops first and that is a disaster in a wet spring. They say hereabout that for every day you delay sowing your barley after April Fool's day you lose a hundredweight of yield. As there are thirty days in April

40

and they're all gone it is easy to see that Big Hamish is too late to get a record year. A whole hundredweight per day may be too high an estimate of the loss but Mossie (who passes as the expert in matters of grain) says Hamish's aim this year should be to get his seed back.

Of course yield doesn't matter with the 'bloo flooers'. With linseed the crop doesn't matter anyway as you get the £240 an acre just to sow it. But even there Hamish is in trouble.

He has two hundred acres of good snipe shooting down by the sea at Cruden Bay and he has ambitions to grow the bloo flooers there. The seeds are bought, the machinery is poised but, as the heavens pour forth and the tide rises steadily, poor Hamish's frustration is complete.

The only remaining hope is that the Boneheads of Brussels come out soon with a new regime for rice.

May 18,1992

Playing all the wrong cards

I WAS watching my latest batch of weaners proudly when the Breadwinner said, with more than a hint of disapproval, "I see you're back to twist, twist, burst."

Players of pontoon will recognise the scenario. In the effort to get as near as possible to twenty-one they keep taking another card until they go right over the top and lose all their money. And the Breadwinner has recognised twist, twist, burst as my principle theory of farm management.

I applied it in the 1970s when I went into Rodenight pigs. That's the system developed by the late Richard Rodenight whereby the sows bring up their litters in little tin huts in what would be grass fields if it weren't for all the pigs in them.

A cousin of mine was reducing his numbers and would sell me thirty sows complete with arcs and feeders... and in pig. It was a delight from start to finish. There were no problems at all. Soon a sea of little pink bodies ebbed and flowed round the park. It was beside the road and all agreed that it was idyllic. This was surely the way to keep pigs.

Even the banker agreed, for that first batch made me enough money to pay for the sows, and all the equipment.

So naturally I twisted. Home came another twenty old sows with more feeders. For the second time in a row we weaned ten pigs per sow. I had surely stumbled upon a money machine.

So I twisted again. The sows were becoming old so I would buy seventy gilts, and put them in pig along with my fifty old sows. That would give me 1,400 piglets which would leave me a fiver each at least....

Burst.

The gilts weren't as clever as the old sows and were determined to live five or six to the hut even when they were pigging and after. Then the piggies started scouring and I had to go round with a barrow to pick up the dead ones every day. The

knacker's van is all right now and again but it got so I didn't even have to call him and I didn't like that.

The vet came of course and I had known no despair in farming like it when I saw this surgeon wandering around in the remains of the 1400, catching the odd pig and squirting some stuff into its mouth. There was no optimism on his part that he had done the few pigs he had treated any good and of course you just can't treat a thousand pigs that way... those that were treated weren't marked so they were just as likely as any other to be next for treatment.

Eventually we stopped them dying by giving the whole lot an in-feed antibiotic. But that proved to be a mistake as well. By far the best paying of that lot of pigs were the ones which died at birth. The rest were never able to thrive and their feed conversion rose from three to five at which they lost money like nothing else.

The banker even started to run out of money. Now that was a serious worry to our feed salesman who offered me free credit till harvest time if I committed my entire harvest to his company.

I didn't go for that. I weaned them, sold the sows fat and sold the arcs.

The TTB management theory was also in force when I started grazing cattle in the early seventies. The first year I went to Oban and bought 42 little stotties at about four or five cwts for about eighty

43

pounds a head and put them on a fine field of sixteen acres. They were dumpy Hereford and Shorthorn types but they thrived like nothing else when they got off the bracken and onto some grass. They all went fat off those sixteen acres and averaged getting on for £200 a head. Another gold mine had clearly been uncovered.

I twisted.

Next year I had more bigger stots and took a park of grass from a neighbour. That year I had over a hundred grazers and I raised them over £100 a head. I also noticed that the best payers were plain cattle that improved.

Next year I would have 200 cattle. At £100 a head that would be £20,000 and I would be rich.

I twisted again.

I took grass all over the place at up to £90 an acre. I bought as plain cattle as I could so that they would have plenty of room to improve. But they declined to accept the challenge and got worse. Only half my cattle went fat and as I had no room to take them in I had to sell those plain brutes on a weak market in November.

It was another burst.

It was the same with the exotic cattle which came flooding into the country in the seventies. I made serious money off the Charolais, twisted and got Simmentals which did even better. So I twisted again and got landed with Blonds, Markies, Chianinas and half a Romagnola which cost £5,000.

So am I set for another burst with the piggies? I am up to 450 of them and the market has vertigo. I am taking in no more. I would like to show the Breadwinner that, with her help, I have conquered the twist, twist, burst system.

Rave-up at the Mart disco

MY CHILDREN never cease to amaze me. This time it was the Wasting Asset. He has led one of the most spectacular diversifications in the history of Scottish Agriculture. He has held the mother and father of all disco raves in the new Mart at Thainstone.

The Aberdeen and Northern has now got this huge mart complex near Inverurie. It is the most modern of buildings for the oldest of marketing methods and it is a considerable overhead. They are on the look out for new uses for the place and have already a Sunday market and have hosted a very successful Bothy Concert in one of the main rings.

So naturally, when the Wasting Asset went along to see about hiring the car auction shed for an all-night disco, he got a fair hearing. Mind you, that was nearly blown when somebody held a secret rave just outside the town in a disused henhouse with no roof. There had been 400 ravers, no policing, one hell of a noise, and with no car parking facilities they had blocked a minor road and in barging into a field and parking there they scared a troop of camping Brownies.

The Provost swore to stamp this sort of thing out and the citizens of Inverurie were scandalised. Things looked black for the mart's new diversification. But eventually the authorities were persuaded that if the all night dance were held in decent premises, properly supervised by the police, monitored by the noise pollution people, all just might be well.

I don't really think they were expecting many from the middle-aged group but we had to go. Mossie, the Red Rooster and myself were a little self-conscious as we entered the Mart. It is certainly the first time we have been frisked...we are shareholders after all.

As we stood feeling a bit awkward in the darkened smoke-filled room, watching the heaving and gyrating which passes for dancing nowadays, one of the many policemen came up and shouted kindly above the racket, "Na, boys. There's nae mart today."

We had done our best to blend in. We none of us had our jackets or ties on and, while Mossie had brown brogues and the Rooster had on his cowboy boots, knowing that trainers were the thing I had looked out my old gym shoes. But surprisingly we still stood out among the ravers. I suppose the police are trained in that sort of thing.

The Rooster was fascinated by the dancing, particularly the high energy efforts of a little girl who was wearing baggy shorts, basketball boots, a teeshirt which had once been white, and beads.

"Where does she get the energy," he said simply. Somebody said something about ecstasy whereupon Mossie came to life, "Is that a new variety o' ile seed rape?"

We tried the bar at £1.50 a can for beer then beat a hasty retreat. At £15 a head it seemed poor value for the 700 youngsters to dance or sit on the concrete floor. The papers described it as an 'Upmarket Rave'... something like the Midsummer Ball at Cambridge University perhaps, but it was nothing like that. There was just as much litter but no drunkenness. Still, the ravers seemed pleased, there was no trouble, the mart made an undisclosed four figure sum and I've got the Wasting Asset's rent money for next month and the hire of the farm truck and his share (95%) of the phone bill.

Mossie has been down to the Pig and Poultry Event at Stoneleigh. He was lucky to get this year after scouring for a fortnight after the Fair of 1990. But he thought the Fair a much cleaner event than the Rave. He was taken, particularly, by a shower unit the Germans have for their sows. Whenever she feels like a freshen up the German sow just trots along to the shower unit and stands on this grid and on comes an automatic shower.

The Germans claim that the more fastidious sowfrau are taking as many as six showers a day. This freedom leads to happier sows, bigger litters, more milk and a less pungent piggery. "You canna even get the FOLK up in Aberdeenshire to take a shower eence a week and the Gerry pigs are showering six times a day," says Mossie. "It's exciting times we live in."

And he's getting the manufacturers of the sow shower to organise a trip to

Germany to see it in action. I am wondering if there is any hope that the Breadwinner will stop me - I really don't think I am strong enough for a sailing with the boys round Bavaria on a sea of white wine.

And back at Little Ardo there is an air of expectancy. As June the first approaches the bulls are girding their loins and the girls are showing regular signs of restlessness. I feel a bit sorry for our Simmental because he's landed across a high fence from the thirty heifers that Rastus the Black bull is to serve in June. Argus paces up and down the fence with love in his eye and makes little moaning noises to the girls. If only I could tell him how close the first of June is it might settle him.

When they were all in for worming the other day I heard him say to Rastus as they passed in the crush, "Did ye ever mak love thru a barbed wire fence?"

"No," said the Black bull.

"Well ye've no missed much," said Argus, sulkily.

47

Everyone in tizzy over rape forms

THERE ARE those who say our discussions at the Salmon Inn are just an excuse for a booze-up. Well sometimes they could be forgiven, but not this Sunday. It was all about MacSharry and the new ways being brought in by the European Economic Community.

What has really set the boys' teeth on edge is the rape forms. Until this year the EEC has given the rape seed crushers a big subsidy for each tonne they used and that raised their enthusiasm for buying the stuff and sent the British price up to as much as three times the world price. All that is gone. Now they are going to give us £175 an acre to grow the stuff and let us sell it for what it is worth.

The problems have come in claiming those acreage payments. No one seems able to understand what to do and we have proof that that is to be expected. Newton was actually the first from this area to tackle his form. He took it in to the Department and filled it in there. He pro-

nounced himself 'cross' therefor, when the form came back sometime later as it was wrongly filled in. "But it can't be. I filled it in with your help."

"But you were our first and we didn't know at that time what was required."

Newton got crosser and crosser in the way that only an aristocrat can and the form was rejected again before all was well. If he who did his early training in the City of London had problems, it is no wonder I suffered. First there were the maps. You need them to get the correct acreages. A complete set would cost me over a hundred pounds and I was keen to avoid that. I tried the library who put me on to the Roads Department. They were very helpful but had one map missing. I then tried the College of Agriculture who sent me to the Mart's estate agency. Eventually I went to the map shop and got the missing map only to find that the field in question is quite out of date. There are no dykes left in it

and half has been built on but the map shows the field intact.

Anyway I got what I thought was all I needed and proceeded to the Department. With only six days till the deadline I didn't want to risk having it rejected. When I got to the relevant floor I could hardly get out of the lift for the queue of farmers waving their forms and their maps. When it was my turn I was soon glad that I had filled the form in in pencil. It made the rubbing out so much easier. Then there was the map. I had forgotten to define the arable acreages in blue and red pencil. And then there was the argument about the word 'arable'.

My dictionary says that means 'ploughable' so I proceeded to put the lines right round the farm. Wrong again. If you read the form properly you see that arable means "Under the plough in 1989." So I had to rub out my lines and that's not easy with coloured crayon.

And everyone was the same. In my two hours there I don't think there was a soul who had done the job right. There were three girls from the Department helping and I must take my hat off to them. How they kept up the good-humoured banter I don't know.

They are going to need all their charm though if we don't get better at the forms

49

for we'll have similar claims to do for wheat and barley before long.

I told George Gray about the crush at the Department so he was prepared for the worst. He normally parks at the station, runs past the pay as you go box, sprints up to the office and gets back before the traffic warden. But after my warning he decided that, just this once, he would put in not one but two pounds for tickets. But when he got to the Department it was closed for Whitsun.

And Mossie had trouble too. He said he never saw a man smile so much as the man in the map shop. He is making a fortune. But when Mossie arrived, a bulb in his map copying machine had fused. Now Mossie has 400 acres to claim so he was getting nervous, "Well get anither een," he said. The man got on to Glasgow who wanted £17.45 to deliver a new bulb. "I'm not paying that for delivery of a one pound bulb. Send it by post."

Mossie was flabbergasted, "But your losin a fortune waiting for the post."

When all was fixed and our man came back his bill was £480. "What? That's half a grand!" And he wasn't exaggerating at all. For when he got back to his car he had a twenty pound parking ticket.

One of the worst problems is taking two percent off the field acreages. That is what the Department wants us to allow for dykes and missed bits. With all the confusion over which maps to use (Because they've all got different acreages) it is difficult enough for any of us. But poor Big Hamish is just beginning to get to grips with how much one percent is. It is far too early to start him on the mysteries of two percent.

There is one good thing though. All the new maps show acreages down slightly. That has happened because they now do the measuring elecronically with lasers. Surveyers trudging about with 22 yard lengths of chain gave you more acres because they went down into every wadie and up over every knowe.

It means we'll have fewer acres to claim but Mossie is delighted. "That's where we've been gaun wrang", he exclaimed in delight when he saw the truth, "Too mony acres. We'll get great yields this year wi' the less measurements."

Courting hares provide welcome break to problems of setaside

SPRING HAS given way to summer. The crops have never looked so well and the bulls are in. There are thirty cows and thirty-five heifers with two bulls now and they make a brave sight. I shudder to think about nine months hence but that is a long time away.

And it is not just the bull who is at work. On my early walk this morning I saw a sight that has become much less common. Two brown hares were in courtship. I love to watch them and it is years since we had great numbers on the farm. When I was a lad we just had to go to the first field to get a choice of hares for the soup and my father and I once counted seventeen hares in the Byre Park.

In those days the typical mating scene was two or even three hares fighting while, some fifty yards away, would be a female sitting demurely

awaiting the outcome. There was no competition this morning and I was gladdened by them.

I needed gladdening too, because of this damned setaside.

My far neighbour and former Member of Parliament, Hamish Watt, is in trouble over setaside. He once wrote of the man who was emigrating with tears in his eyes. "Homosexuality used to be an offence, now they've legalised it and I'm getting out before it is made compulsory." Hamish said that story encapsulated how he felt about setaside. So he now has, in honour, to emigrate. For we can escape setaside no longer if we want government support.

The boys are not pleased and the discussion group on Sunday was devoted to discussing how we would react to having to put 15% of our arable land down to weeds.

The general consensus was that it was a bad business. It was levelling the good farmers like Mossie and the Rooster back towards middling farmers like myself. Though I couldn't see that that was all bad, I had to agree that it is a funny thing in a world that is always on about competitiveness and efficiency.

Anyway, Newton is going to rotate his setaside so that what it will mean, in effect, is a return to the old fallow field system. That way, which is still common in America, you left a proportion of the farm each year and gave it a rest while the fertility built up. He says he'll get bigger crops after fallowing and save manure.

That's no use to Mossie though. He's spent eleven years establishing disease-free wheat fields and has ninth-year rape. So he can't possibly rotate. Mossie's plan is to buy another farm and set that aside. Fine for some.

But poor Big Hamish is in a real lather about the deal. As one who doesn't know percentages he smells trouble coming in setting aside. He has no idea how many acres 15% is. All he knows is that it's a good deal more than the 2% he had to take off last week's claim for the rape acreage payments.

And I am determined to grow something on my setaside. My ancestors demand it. They did not drain and stone this land, nor did they carry seaweed from the coast to fertilise this farm so that I could grow weeds. God knows I grow enough of them already without setting aside the seventh part of my inheritance for weeds.

I would be sad to have to put land that can grow four tonnes of wheat down to trees but it could come to that. Much better would be the growing of a crop that escapes the net. You can graze horses on setaside. And you can grow commercial hay as long as it is eaten by horses. And wasn't there a Lord Somebody in the south who had a volunteer crop of wheat which he was allowed to harvest provided he fed it to his pheasants?

I don't have that many pheasants but I do have a large number of rats. Would that do? Surely a rat is just as worthy of EEC support as a pheasant. It is better as, being inedible, the rat doesn't add to the food mountains. Or are pheasants subsidised in this way because people shoot them? I'm sure we could teach sportsmen to shoot rats for a change.

Or one could just cheat. I have a neighbour who had a very fair crop of volunteer rape in his setaside. He asked the Ministry if he could use his combine to do the statutory topping. "Oh, yes. That will be alright as long as you dump any grain you get." So he 'dumped' the grain in his barn. That seems quite a possible way out of the dilemma. After all, the best crop of rape I had last year was eighteen acres of volunteer Cobra. It yielded 23 cwts which was a lot last year at Little Ardo.

The other thing that was scandalising the boys this week was the picture of King Arthur's Death Pit that appeared in one of the Sunday papers. The King is one of our mega-farmers and they carried a picture of the pit into which he throws his deadstock. This is just a hole in the ground. Although it is behind a seven foot fence it is uncovered. The theory is that the carcases rot there and it never needs emptying. Apparently, this method of disposing of stock has been passed by the authorities locally but it doesn't make for a pretty picture.

It was horrendous in fact. What appeared to be hundreds of pigs, lambs and at least two bloated cows could be clearly seen.

The boys were horrified. Crookie had spent all day helping at the industry's 'Food and Farming' event at Thainstone. "It's a bit of a waste of time working on our image if folk are going to get caught with a thing like that."

That motion was carried unanimously.

June 15, 1992

A day off is hard to come by

I HAVE a neighbour with whom I wage the tiresome old argument about whether farmers are obscenely rich or in dire straights. I try to tell him that the illusion that we are all rolling in it stems from the fact that eighty percent of us have had to leave the industry since the war. Only the lucky few survive so he isn't seeing most of the pain. I try to tell him that a farmer who drives a Daimler when the Range Rover is in for repair is no more typical than the farmer who has no car at all and uses his tractor when he ventures from home.

But he just won't have it. We are rich, we are feather-bedded and as such we deserve all we don't get.

He was at it again this week and just because I was invited to a farming wedding on a Wednesday. "Only the rich can have a wedding on a Wednesday. The rest of us have to wait until Saturday to get a day off."

That really got me going, "What the hell difference does it make to the likes of me what day it is? I know you solicitors obey the commandment 'Five days shalt thou labour, on the sixth thou shalt go to weddings and other diversions' but, as far as I'm concerned, there is just as much work to be done on the seventh day as on any other."

And it's true. To the vast majority of us farmers who are running one-man bands, any day off is as hard to come by as any other.

Of course that wasn't true for the principals at the wedding for that was a joining of two of the successful and perhaps even rich farming families in the county. The groom was a Massie from Blelack, the very successful Aberdeen Angus and Charolais breeders and the man picking up the tab for the do was Bill Ferguson of Rothiebrisbane who is high up in the Scottish Agricultural College and the Milk Board and grows very expensive seed barley.

As it was a Massie-Ferguson wedding I think the least the company should have done was to give the

ONLY RICH FARMERS CAN HAVE A WEDDING ON A WEDNESDAY

couple a new tractor to get them started.

It was a splendid do held, as is becoming more and more the fashion in a tent on the lawn. And some tent. This was a far cry from the marquee we used to dance in forty years ago in the pleasure park at Methlick. It was lined with silks like a sheik's boudoir, you didn't trip on the joins when you were dancing and, in a major departure from the new tradition, it wasn't cold. Every tattie shed for miles around had been plundered for it's hot air blower.

The paymaster for the day (who must be pleased that he has now run out of daughters, having married three of them off in rapid succession) is a man I like.

He is full of old wisdoms. For example he described someone of whom he didn't wholly approve as being "The sort of man who is always borrowing machinery and puts the tractor back empty and the cement mixer back full".

He told me a fine story which I hope you'll enjoy even half as much as I did.

It concerns a renowned and much loved Gillie who was retiring after fifty-two years in the service of Lord So-and-So. When it came to making his speech of thanks for the gold watch Old Jock got to his feet but was overcome with emotion. He stood in front of a mixed company which varied from his peers to peers of the realm, and try as he might all he could get out was tears.

After some little time Lord So-and-So rose and leading the applause said, "Man Jock, I've heard better speeches but never one that came so truly from the heart."

Back on the farm and coupling is much in evidence there too. The bulls are sticking manfully to their task, though how Rastus the Black bull can stand having his current project surrounded by her thirty-four excited cousins, I don't know. If he can just stick it for another week the load should decrease.

The rabbits are hard at it too. We have a swarm of tiny bundles eating up the lettuces at the moment and they have shown up yet another flaw in my children. They'll never make peasants. Even the Wasting Asset, with a history of mayhem behind him, won't let me shoot the little darlings. Next year I'll get him to dig the garden and plant the lettuces. That should cure him.

And the partridges are nesting. There is a pair just opposite the single cotter house on the brae leading down to the village. I didn't find the nest but they flew out from the same spot where almost fifty years ago I first found a partridge's nest. I remember counting the eggs and finding that there were fourteen or thirteen depending on which side of the nest I started at. At either rate there would, I thought, be lots and lots of partridges in that field next year.

I was disappointed. Always there was one nest and one only. Some years the winter was severe and we thought they would be killed off. And once we had a young man who shot every game animal on the place. Yet each year there was a pair and one pair only on the brae. That is the sad truth about nature's bounty; the few are born to live but the majority die young.

It is paradoxical that it is only in man-made systems, where animals are reared to be killed, that they have a good chance of reaching maturity.

Highland Show

WHEN YOU see all those great beasts parading round the show ring this week I'd like you to remember that those animals are not born to be docile. That calm scene which many of us find so moving, is the product of many hours of often painful labour.

It was certainly so with Gudron, the enormous Simmental heifer I took to the Highland in 1979. All over Scotland and indeed the world there were people looking forward to the Highland Show but not Gudron, and she was damned if she would walk on a halter.

Of course the right way to train a beast is to put a halter on it in its first six weeks and keep at it through its life. But that only happens where there are plenty of staff and, though in those days I did have two men, there was no time for that sort of planning at Little Ardo.

In Canada I had seen them tying the beast to a donkey. That soon taught the trainee to move when the donkey pulled on the halter. But we didn't have a donkey then and anyway, with Gudron, an ele-phant would have been more appropriate.

The first move was to tie her up in the old byre where my father used to keep a few illegal cows that were supposed to be dry but whose milk always found its way into the cans. We talked soothingly to her, pampered her with suppies of cake and used a stiff brush on her itchy bits. That was a poor success. For days Gudron fought the sail and bayed.

When she had calmed down a bit we kept her short of water so that she would willingly walk to the trough at the end of the byre. We would then walk her back to her stall for some of her favourite mash. That usually works but not this time. She bounced me from stall to stall and wall to wall until by chance she landed back in her stall and I got her tied up again.

We then tried two halters with a third man holding a neck rope at the back. It was still no use. Down went Gudron's head and up went her tail and off she went with the ropes hanging off like streamers from a football supporters' bus.

Then we tied her to the back of a tractor. Not even Gudron could resist seventy-two horsepower so she did move forward but it was more like skiing than walking as she braced her front legs and slid along the road. We had to stop very shortly as she was wearing out her hoofs and would soon have been down to the quick.

The breakthrough came the day we tried to wash Gudron. That meant a trip of some two hundred yards from the little byre to the wash-bay. We put gates in all the right places so that there was nowhere but the right way for her to run. I untied her and she set off, head down, tail up and me hanging on like grim death. As she charged down the close my feet only touched the ground every ten yards or so. She only just missed the door of the wash bay which was more than I did.

But we got there and I got her tied up. I slumped on a bale with a curious feeling of relief and mild shock. Gudron had made her first journey according to my plan and, as compared to my budget, with a considerable saving in time.

She must have enjoyed the wash for she walked back to her stall and her mash. We were on our way to the Highland.

We grew to love each other at Ingliston as I struggled all day every day to keep the grass and the mash going in and to deal with the flow of muck coming out. I would spend hours at a time washing and grooming her and, when I took my hangover to see her each morning at six, she would lick it with the great rasping tongue of hers. It didn't really cure anything but it seemed like affection and it did take the mind of the woodpeckers eating away behind the eyeballs.

And my love of Gudron grew when it came to the judging. The liveliness she had shown in her training did her no harm in the ring. She held her head up like a queen and looked alertly about her as if fascinated by the question of which beast was going to be second.

So we had a good show after all. But one of the troubles with showing is that when you have fed them up for the show you have done the cattle no favours when it comes to calving. Gudron was huge and we did worry that she might stick.

I nipped down to the field before our guests came that Saturday night and sure enough her udder was like a

rubber glove with a gallon of water in it. She was restless and footing. One of the guests and I went down to see her in the last of the evening light and sure enough the water was off and there was just the hint of a foot sticking out.

Normally I'd have tried my hand inside to ensure that all was well but Gudron had a look in her eye that I'd seen before when she dragged me through the close. I was reminded of the Highland doctor's midwifery kit which consisted of a half bottle and a pair of slippers. We withdrew to the fireside and our thirst.

There is no doubt the old doctor's policy was right for Gudron's confinement. When we went down at midnight she was licking up at her fine heifer calf. That was a cause for celebration which meant our guests were slow to leave and that the morning broke delicately.

It is just as well I didn't go again to the field till morning. Had I done there would have had to be more celebration. Certainly next morning she was suckling two heifer calves and I wasn't seeing double.

Rastus gets 'Dear John' from ladies

I'M NOT too happy about things today.

First, there seems to be something going wrong with the bulling. You know that Rastus, the black bull bought for the heifers at great expense at the Spring Show, is looking after thirty-three of my heifers and three from a neighbour. Well he's keen enough on the contract but I'm not too sure about the heifers.

You see, in the next field there are two pure Simmental cows with three calves. One has a set of twin five month old bulls and the other has an eight month old bull. In the last week three of Rastus's maidens have come in season, and jumped the dyke to get at Young Lochinvar.

Now, I don't know if they got out when they looked in Rastus's eye or whether they just took the view that once was enough of him. You could hardly blame them as Rastus is almost bald in his summer clothes whereas the calf has a gorgeous coat of Adonis hair. Certainly the three have been bulled for I have seen their tails sticking out but it will be a great shame if they have Simmental calves.

We put them in with the black bull because they are not big heifers and we wanted them to have small Aberdeen-Angus calves, not great continental brutes. When I told big Hamish about it he told me that, as it was only a little Simmie bull, I'd have nothing to worry about and anyway that Rastus is a big brute.

Unfortunately, as I understand it, genetic size is nothing to do with the size of the bull at the moment of impact, so I will have to watch those three carefully and get the Wasting Asset to make a better job of the fence next time than he did last time.

And I'm also not pleased by the effect the new Common Agricultural Policy proposals will have on my strategy for my hill cows. I have bought Hereford-Friesian calves and bulled them early to give me small cows which I can cram onto my ground to get as many hill cow subsidies and as many beef special premia per acre as I can.

But now they are to bring in quotas, if Big Hamish is right - and he's the local Farmer's Union President. So if I'm only allowed to have forty cows, the clever thing will be to have as big cows as possible to maximise the size of the calves and to maximise the farrow cow price. So whichever bull has got my thirty-three heifers I am liable to be wrong.

Then there's the pigs. I still like them in principle but I fear that they will start to stink again when I get a final tally on the current lot. They are staying alive, they look well but they are staying on the farm too long. I am putting away a big batch next week and they'll have been with me for thirteen weeks against a target of nine and a budget of ten. That smacks to me of a poor conversion rate - and a loss. The only hope is that they are not eating much and I am pessimistic about that, though I suppose it could be with the mild weather.

Then again, I've been reminded that, like most of the rest of the world, I am not as smart as I think. This is my first year of spraying my crops and that is proving a very good move. I save two pounds and fifty pence an acre every time I yoke the sprayer and I get the timing of every application right to the day. If I had had my own sprayer last year I'm confident I would be a richer man than I am today.

On the other hand I might have been blind or had some dreadful lung disease.

You see I have not bothered with all the precautions you are supposed to take in applying chemicals. No rubber gloves, no face mask, no nothing.

Well, up till now that non-system has worked tolerably. I have had the odd headache after spraying and a dryness in my throat but nothing more. But last week's spraying for beetles in the oilseed rape changed my attitude. I suppose that shouldn't surprise me for if the stuff kills beetles it is unlikely to do me much good.

And where the beetles just got one shower of insecticide I had it for half of three hours. You see there was a fair breeze blowing. When I was going into the wind my air was clear. But when the wind was in my back I carried a cloud of the stuff along with

me. I was in sore need of a mask for I couldn't shut the back window of the tractor as I need it open to get at the controls.

By night the old eyes were tight shut against any further invasion and my face was red and stinging. I can tell you I will have the protective gear before it is time to give the wheat its headspray.

But if I am not so sure about my farming just now, Mossie is on a high. He has solved the setaside problem. He has bought a farm, of just the right size to fulfil all the requirements to set aside a sixth of his land in combinable crops to qualify for agricultural subsidies.

Of course, how much you can believe I'm not too sure but the setaside farm is said to be well bought. The setaside money will pay the banker and leave profit once he has sold the wood, the steading, the house and the duckpond.

"Setaside? Setaside? What's that again? Oh! It's exciting times we live in." If Mossie says that once more I'll do him in.

My view from the hill was never better

MY COUNTRY is looking well. I would venture to say that it has never looked better. And sitting here at Little Ardo, on top of the little hill that shelters the village of Methlick from the north wind, I am in an ideal position to see it.

This land has been farmed for at the very least three thousand years and probably five. Not a mile down the Ythan valley from where I sit there are stone circles made by the Beaker people and evidence of their farming. Not a mile upstream, on the Braes o' Gight, flint arrowheads have been found by the dozen. And in the middle distance I can see the farm on which the stone circle stands, round which the religious and social life of a community which predated Christ revolved.

Now, I know that many people's idea of beauty in a landscape is wilderness. I have often seen what they might mean. I have seen it in the snows of Alaska, the deserts of North Africa, the Italian Alps and even the West Highlands of Scotland. But, to a farmer, beauty in the land is order. It is the triumph of his choice of flora and fauna over that which would have occurred in his absence.

And by our standards as husbandmen what I see from my window is order, it is looking well and it is a triumph.

The village which lies below me used to be ringed with tiny fields each of which was the property of one of the tradesmen. They kept their milk cow there and perhaps a few sheep and a stot or two. All but one has been absorbed into the bigger farms round about and, in fact, we have taken on five such fieldies. And the one remaining tradesman's field is the only place I can see where nature is even putting up a fight let alone winning. The publican's park is more than a mile away and yet I can clearly see the dark

THE FUTURE?

SETASIDE
BY ORDER
EEC

Turnbull

green clumps which are huge Scotch thistles. The limeless and nitrogen-starved ley is a sickly light green with just a hint of buttercup yellow showing through.

But the rest of my country is looking so well. We've had the weather for it this year but it seems to me that it is more than that. It is as though the shocks of recent years had made us keener and keener to do the job right.

The harsh yellow of the winter rape is gone and the spring stuff is just starting to flower. So the countryside is a tapestry of greens. It ranges from the pale, tender shoots showing through the yellow in the late cut silage, through the bearded golden green of the Pleasante barley, the

deeper green of the spring barley, the grazing, and the winter wheat to the browny green of the crop of Igri that a neighbour who hasn't heard the news is insisting on growing.

Soon the land will start to turn to harvest but at the moment it is all growth and promise.

Of course there are blemishes on our husbandry. There are farms where the fences have fallen down. There is no manpower to put them up again and no need. You don't need a good fence to keep yavel crops in. And, sadder because they can never recover, the drystane dykes are in a bad way and getting worse.

My grandfather, with

whom I lived during the war when my parents were away dealing with the threat from Mr Hitler, used to make much of the farmer's desire to make two blades of grass grow where only one had grown before. That was his credit to the white clover. But we have certainly done that. He used to go for the thirty hundredweight crop and now we are pretty disappointed with sixty. The way my crops are looking just now I intend to sulk if I don't average four tonnes this year for the first time.

And it is not just in its fertility that my countryside is looking well. Compared with when I was a boy we live in a forest. I remember how enchanted I was with Perthshire when I was eight because the farmland was garlanded with trees. Aberdeenshire, on the other hand, couldn't spare the land. We still don't waste much good land on trees but as I look down on the Ythan valley today there are healthy clumps of trees everywhere and not just in the policies of the Lords of Aberdeen.

Yes it is looking quite wonderful today. And today I am taking a long look at it. For my land may never look so well again in early summer. It may never look as well again as it did this spring but I wasn't aware of the extent of the danger then. I appreciate the danger fully now so at harvest time I'll be taking another long look at my country for there may never be another harvest like it.

We face a danger that is easily the worst since Robert the Bruce paid us a visit. He set fire to absolutely everything and killed every man woman and child who could not flee so that has to be the worst that has happened to our farms. But the new European arrangements are going to mean setting a minimum of fifteen percent of our combined land back to the wilderness.

We could laugh at voluntary setaside and watch the few who had land which should never have been in crop in the first place and which the market was taking out of production anyway get a few pounds from the EEC.

That was a waste and a farce but it didn't matter. Now we cannot avoid it and it does matter. We are going to grow one blade of grass where two grew before. Our land is about to become a mess.

How to sip gently and survive

I WAS just about ready to abandon my remaining chores and set off for the show about dinner-time on the Thursday when I remembered that the barley beef nuts I had ordered hadn't yet arrived. I phoned the suppliers.

"Oh yes. They were delivered yesterday."

I guessed at once what had happened. The cattle feed had been delivered all right but into the bin which feeds the pigs.

Now, I am not easily upset but the thought of what a sudden change of diet would be doing to my three hundred piggies did take the edge off my excitement at going off to the Show. These highly bred beasts don't need much excuse to drop dead. They can die of shock when they go from one carefully designed pig diet to another. What would the change to cattle feed do? And how on earth did it happen?

Unfortunately, there are two versions of that.

The lorry driver says he was directed by the Wasting Asset. He then handed over the delivery note and the Asset disappeared into the house.

The Asset's version is rather different. When the lorry arrived the Asset shouted out "Is that pig feed?" and, having been assured of that, he asked if it was in bulk to which the driver also seemed to assent. He then pointed out where the pig feed bin was, collected the delivery note and disappeared.

Those details are of historic and legal interest only. In the meantime I was faced with three hundred hungry pigs which were being offered cattle-feed, half a dozen steers who were being offered starvation, and a burning desire to disappear to Edinburgh.

A quick check of the piggery revealed that they hadn't started to die yet but that the beef nuts were already coming through in the feed. Indeed it seemed that the mixture was nearly neat cattle feed. So that solved the problem of what to give the barley beefers.

The cattle-feed merchants agreed to send out a couple of tonnes of their pig feed as I couldn't raise my usual supplier who was already away to the Show. Then I left the Wasting Asset to bag the three tonnes as it came through. I am told he gave up at eleven o'clock, but by that time I was drowning my sorrows in Edinburgh. I have never been good at delegation but if nothing else comes out of the incident with the pig feed at least I have made a start.

It ruined the whole strategy of the Highland. That is to have one working day in which investigations are made among the trade stands as to what bargains are to be had. And at the college and other advisory stands as to what grants are available to help us get more for growing less.

There would then be one social day set aside for renewing old acquaintances and making new ones.

Now, because of that damned cattle feed, I had missed the working day. I should have left it at that but I tried to combine the two on the Friday and that was a poor success. Because we were trying to see as much as possible we were only on each stand for the minimum time to see it and have, out of politeness, one drink.

Given time, a man like me can sip gently and survive. But with the necessity of rushing off to the next venue all the time, and the frustration of trying to get Mossie, Crookie and Red Rooster to keep up, I was, by the evening, tired and emotional. By five o'clock on Saturday morning, when I rose to come home, I was saying what I have said before and will no doubt say oftentimes more, "Never again."

Mind you, I do remember that I was told a great lot of stories at the Show and that I liked the stories very well. Unfortunately I can only remember two.

One was about the duck shooters who were puzzling over why they had come home with empty game bags. Eventually Paidrich agreed with Mick when he said, "I tink maybe we weren't throwing the dogs up high enough."

And the other concerns the legendary figure of John Robertson the farmer of Drumnagair in the Mearns. You will remember my telling you about the time he took the double-barrelled shotgun to the football that was being

67

kicked in the field beside his young staigs.

Well, this concerned the time that old Drumlie went to the Bonspiel at Edinburgh and, knowing her husband full well, Mrs Robertson had sent one of his sons with him to make sure that his father came home in due time and in good order.

All was well intentioned until it came time to leave. Then the old man would come later - and then much later - until the son made sadly for home alone.

The next morning Wull felt safe for a long lie, the better to recover from his own efforts at the curling. After all, the old man was safely in Edinburgh.

But he had reckoned without old Drumlie's constitution and resourcefulness. At seven o'clock the dreaded voice was roaring up the stairs, "What the hell time o' day's this tae be lying in yer bed Wull?"

The old man, had finished his revels in the toon and made his way to Waverly Station. From there he had caught a goods train North. Sharing the driving and a half bottle he had made speedy progress. As was usual for him, he'd got the train to make an unscheduled stop and walked across the fields of Drumnagair and been home for yokin time.

July 13, 1992

Push to be first was all wrong

THE FARMS of Little Ardo and Wardford glower across the Ythan valley at one and other. We are on the North side of the valley and look down on the village and across to Wardies. They are on the South side and look across and, I like to think, up to us. We have a gentle Southern exposure while they are North-lying.

Now, that topography has given the farmers of Little Ardo an invaluable advantage in what has often been a serious rivalry. There was nothing we could do about the fact that they had a forty-acre field whereas we had nothing more than twenty acres - except deny it. And that we did despite the fact that there it obviously was in all its vastness. I remember hoeing turnips in our Piggery Park which looks directly over at Wardie's prairie and listening to the men pouring scorn on the very idea that they had anything above our twenty-acre.

That sort of esoteric discussion could go on all day and did indeed last for almost the whole yoking.

But we did tend to get our own back at harvest. There was tremendous rivalry to be started first, redding roads with the scythe. If you were beaten with that you could still be first to start the binder or better still to be first finished. Then you would want to be first into the leading home of the sheaves and first to throw the winter sheaf up onto the last stack for the year.

My father and the farmer of Wardford in his time, James Presly, carried on a rather public battle over who was first. They used to meet at the shop each morning when they were down collecting the papers. The old men who act as delivery boys in Methlick would be entertained to the well worn banter.

If we had finished leading the night before, my father would taunt James that this was surely no time of year to be harvesting and James would reply that we would

see about that when the Little Ardo stacks started to heat and had to be taken down again. And if James got started first with the binder my father would ask if he was expecting the price of oats to fall that he was cutting it for silage.

Of course having the South-lying farm, my father tended to have the advantage so that while he was the most adept at the taunts, James Presly had to become the master of the riposte. Like the time that we were so far ahead and the wheat was so dry that we decided to thrash it straight out of the stook instead of stacking it and thrashing in the idle days of winter.

My father knew the eyes of the countryside were upon us and he liked that fine. From where he stood, thrashing out of the stook was almost as good as having one of those new-fangled combined harvesters that they had on some of the braw farms down in the Mearns.

But to James Presly this was a sign that the old man's ways were catching up with him and that he was short of money. So short that he could not wait for a thrash in decent time but must hurry his grain to market. "Aye John," he said with a sorrow he did not feel and in a voice that was easily loud enough, "Wi that fine corn yard we've got at Wardies we could maybe have helped you oot if you're short."

There is no record of my old man's reply which is a

70

pity.

I tell you that because it could not happen today. That sort of not unfriendly but serious competition is one of the many things of the past - or it should be. For one thing there aren't the men on the farms to enjoy the rivalry. On that day of the great debate on whether our twenty-acre park was bigger than Wardie's forty-acre park there were six of us at the hoe and the other five had the time to raise their eyes from the job and survey the countryside.

Nowadays there is no one with whom I can share my fantasies and, if someone comes with some enormous power tool to help, he makes too much noise to allow conversation and has to watch his machine too carefully to contemplate Wardie's acres.

But it's more than that. The push to be first was exactly wrong. That was brought home to me last year when we all had that terrible disaster with the oil seed rape. We had one ten-acre field that had so much sclerotinia that it turned brown and then black in early August. We

harvested a pathetic fifteen hundredweights which only seemed to weigh about twelve in the brutal light of the merchant's returns. Our pain was only eased slightly by the fact that Wardie, who had also had a lot of Tapidor, the most badly affected crop, had fared even worse. He had beaten us to it. He had harvested his even earlier.

But in the meantime, Mossie the Grain Baron, was wondering if he would ever get harvest as his green and healthy crops would not die but just kept on filling until he could harvest crops of up to 36 hundredweights. It was not the one whose crops were ripe first who was the good farmer. The trick nowadays is to keep the stuff growing and filling as long as possible.

If young Wardie gets going before us this harvest I shall say to him, if I see him at the shop, "Aye Wardie. The barley's died on you I see. You winna need to be so mean wi the sprays next year."

Of course in the new rivalry, I am at a disadvantage with my South-lying farm.

Bertie had a collie's eye for the hill

"BUT BERTIE," says I, "it's eighteen miles home. How on earth are you going to be there at five o'clock when it's four already." The digger which he was driving and which was our transport was unsafe at five miles an hour and he was going to have to average eighteen.

It was a serious problem. With the Laird and the banker coming to see about the transfer of the tenancy he had been threatened with divorce if he was late and we all know how serious that can be to a farmer.

With a steely glint in his eye Bertie pointed fair up the hill. "We'll go ower the hill and doon Glen Terry."

There was no road and indeed no hint that the journey had ever been done on wheels and yet we set off straight up.

To say that I was alarmed is to understate the case altogether. It looked like a one-in-one slope from the ground and I could see no favourable outcome as I hung on to the back of the furiously bucking digger.

After a very short time I decided to walk so that when the inevitable happened I could go for help.

But Bertie seemed to have a Collie's eye for the hill and managed to get a route right up and without so much as a backward sneer at his passenger-of-little-faith. If he had reckoned without the fence that ran the length of the tops and separated one estate from the other he showed no surprise as he came upon it.

"There won't even be a gate. Why should there be. When ever would the people from the one estate want to or be allowed to drive onto the other?"

Wrong again but not that wrong. There was indeed a gate but it was not built for Bertie's digger. When you measured the width of the digger and the width of the gate there was a deficiency of a good foot.

But our man was nothing daunted. To me what followed rivalled the feeding of the five thousand or perhaps

72

the pouring of a pint and a half of milk into a small chocolate bar. Bertie drove the digger at speed at the gate and at an angle of about forty-five degrees. When the front bucket hit the strainer on the far side, the machine (I had never heard of side brakes) leapt to the side and somehow, and in an instant, slewed through the gap and the two strainers snapped shut behind us.

I was allowed no hint that anything remarkable had been achieved but I was allowed to shut the gate.

I then expected Bertie to be able to walk on water and indeed that was almost what was required. For we had some pretty wet peaty land to get through. Only once did we falter and that tried even my new-found faith. We were quickly over the axles in bog.

There seemed no way out but I was wrong yet again. That was the first time I had seen a back acter used as a means of locomotion. The great arm was sent out, sunk deep into the mire and then it bent at the elbow and dragged us down the hill and clear.

To cut a long story short, we got there in time. The tenancy is still secure, indeed Bertie won the championship in the Cross Cattle section at this year's Highland Show,

and the marriage which had just started then is due for its silver jubilee.

I remembered all that this week when the Breadwinner and I took a three-day pre-harvest break up Clova and the hotel bedroom looked out at the face up which Bertie had driven the old digger.

I can't say that it was a well-earned rest because I spent the day before we left with my accountant going over the havoc wrecked by last year's poor crops. You will recall that take-all in half the wheat and sclerotinia in most of the rape cut me down to size. We ended up down £20,000 on the combinable crops and about £6,000 down on costs. In all a loss of over £4,000.

It is true that we farmers are able to get a certain amount of our costs which some might argue are living expenses, counted off before our losses are struck. But even at that it seems a poor return on a farm which would sell for £400, 000. It is minus one per-cent in fact, and even I can't live on that.

And we took two steps in the wrong direction this week. The last heifer I bought in the spring time to make up my numbers, in case the man from the Department came to count my cows, would calve on the day we were due to leave for our wee holiday. She was a feeding heifer which had turned out in calf among those of my cattle buyer Sandy Fowlie.

They were bought on the basis of the beef price; any calf and the peace of mind from knowing my numbers were up were for nothing. I left the Wasting Asset and Potions the chemist and off we went. When I came home it was to find a note from the vet. The heifer would be all right if she would eat and her stiches would come out in three weeks.

Sure enough they'd waited too long before getting the vet and a huge dead Charolais bull calf. Still, the heifer was chewing her cudd when I saw her and seemed one hundred per-cent fit.

The other wrong foot cost about £140. We put away sixty-three baconers, nine of which were just under the new higher weight ranges. If you are outside the range they just steal them. I don't see that we can complain - but I don't like it.

July 27, 1993

Up to the hurdies in nettles

IN THE days when men were men, and a bottle of whisky a day was nothing, the generation before mine went on a great fact-finding tour of England. They went to the agricultural places at Silsoe and Cirencester, they visited some of the great farms in Norfolk, and they raised all kinds of hell among the gentle creatures of those soft Southern lands.

Among those men was Bob Milne of Dykelands, in the Howe of the Mearns. Bob has many claims to fame, but I'll mention three of them. First, in his mid-eighties, he is still scampering round the golf course with a lower handicap than mine; second, he made a million pounds out of selling bulbs to the Dutch; and third, in a culture of tipplers and heroic feats of alcohol recycling he doesn't, and never did, drink.

Now, you might think that such a man would be out of place in a farmers' study tour of England's greener and pleasanter lands in the late 1940s and, to one extent, you could be right.

Certainly there was an occasion when Bob took off on his own for a bit of further sight-seeing while his rowdy friends, including my father, my uncle and his brother-in-laws, got down to serious business in the Star and Garter. He had been away for some time and the party was in full swing - and gales of happy laughter and earnest debate enveloped the street.

As Bob was about to make his re-entry into the society of his brothers, a native asked him, not unkindly, who those gentlemen might be.

"Oh," says Bob, "they're a delegation of Church of Scotland ministers doing a study tour of English Cathedrals." The Englishman was satisfied with the answer and, no doubt, impressed with the splendour of a Church which could boast such men.

I tell you that story because it makes me happiest to think of such men and such times. But today I must tell of melancholy things from my time.

75

Like Sunday morning when the phone rang. I think the phone knows when it is bringing you bad news. It has a domineering, scornful sound. When it's only some little girl phoning to see if the Wasting Asset is coming out to play, it has a delightful, timid little tinkle, but it rang not so on Sunday morning.

And sure enough, "Aye, Charlie. You've a beast oot on the Methlick to Aberdeen road." That made me sad. I was enjoying the splendour of still being in bed at seven, and wondering if I might risk trying the Breadwinner with a cup of tea. Instead, I rushed down to the village to find that the beast had very properly jumped back into the field and that the no-claim discount on my public liability policy was safe.

But I couldn't leave it at that. Beasts don't jump barbed wire fences for nothing, and there was plenty of grass in the field and no sign of a dog that might have been playing. It had to be lack of water. And, indeed, it was. They have been drinking from a spring that rises in that field for a number of years, and when I went to check I found no more than a muddy patch where the spring used to be.

So all I had to do was to find the water-key, find the stop-cock, and reactivate the trough. But that wasn't at all as easy as it may sound. The trough had been cut off for many years, and the Toby which protects the stop-cock was, I remembered, quite a long way from the trough. It was in over the fence among the reeds, rashes, and nettles that garland the river Ythan.

Now, after years of rows for getting my clothes covered with farmyard detritus, I have taken to wearing a boilersuit. I quickly learned to hate the garment because it is so very difficult to get into and, worse still, out of. Also 'boiler' is the word, for in summertime it has been unbearably hot. For that reason I have taken to wearing only minimal clothing under it.

And so, as I cast about in the four-foot high foliage looking for the Toby, I found another objection to the boilersuit - it is no protection against stingy nettles.

I was in no mood, therefore, to hear the raucous tones of the farmer of Mossside."T'hell are ye deein?" I told him, as patiently as I could, that the beasts were dying of thirst and that if only I could find this stop-cock I could solve the problem. An extra pair of feet tramping down the nettles would have

76

been quite a help.

He surveyed me sympathetically from the bridge and said, as sadly as he could, "It's times like this you wish you had stuck in at the school."

I would have put up with anything if he'd given me a hand, but, from the distance of the bridge, it was too much. "I did stick in at school, and I got a prize at the university - and it's a fat lot of use when you're up to the hurdies in nettles and folk just watching from the brig."

"Aye," he said clearly, and then I thought he risked a chuckle before disappearing back to check out the newly tarred dual-carriageway in about to Moss-side.

I thought I had him this week though. There was a great meeting at Inverurie where our NFU representatives answered questions from 250 of us on the MacSharry CAP reforms. I asked if I could buy a farm like Mossie and set that aside instead of my own beloved acres.

"No. You've got to have cultivated the land last year." What joy. So Mossie was beat for once. No chance. The farm he has bought is one he had rented the year before, so he is alright. It is just me and everybody else that is going to be forced to grow weeds.

Statue to MacSharry of Setaside

"WE ARE the working classes now." That was the clear consensus of the boys at the discussion group on Sunday. How our circumstances have changed. Ninety percent of the people of Britain consider themselves middle class, and ten percent are unemployed - so we farmers may even be the entire working class these days.

In my own case it is the old story of rags-to-rags in three generations.

My grandfather was a very skilful farmer and a hard-working man. He had the tenancy of 400 decent, second-class acres from Lord Aberdeen, and no fear of debt. Thus when everyone around him was going broke in the 1920s and 1930s, he was able to borrow money and buy up farms for very little.

That meant he was able to take off his boots for the last time when he was only 34. Men were cheap then; he could get a good man for £20 for a half year, so he hired and concentrated on what he could plan on the backs of envelopes.

All this meant that when my father came victorious out of the army in 1945, the fine farm of Little Ardo was waiting for him. There were six men ready to work a 48-hour week without holidays, and wives who were willing to work in the house and help out at harvest and at the tatties.

So my father did almost all of his farming in thinking mode. He had one foot on the gate, the pipe in his mouth, and gladness in his heart for nature's bounty. That is my favourite image of my father, of the gentleman farmer. He paid £4200 for the title deeds and took £3000 profit in his first year. That was surely better than soldiering against the Hun.

Mind you, in the foolish way of the dreamer, he had

78

thought of working a bit when he came home from the war. He volunteered to fork on the land in his first harvest, but that was a humiliating failure. He and the foreman's wife were making progress that was far too sedate for the grieve, the great Jimmy Low.

With a roar of frustation he came striding across from where he would have been building the ricks - if enough sheaves had been coming home. He snatched the fork from the farmer and proceeded to put up four sheaves at a time until the cart was full. He then banged the fork into the ground at his employer's feet and said, "That's the speed at hairst time."

My father didn't disagree, but he took his boots off for the last time that night and, from then on, held a watching brief.

It was that brief that I wanted when I gave up the University of Strathclyde in the early 1970s and made for my roots. I'd work for a couple of years, just till I got everything working like clock-work, and then I'd throw away the boots before I was 40.

And so it was. When Mrs Thatcher came to power I had put the stock up from 4 to 700 cattle, the average age of the tractors was down from 15 years to ten, and the overdraft was up from £10 to £1000 an acre. I was ready to be thoroughly middle class.

I suppose it may have been something to do with the overdraft, but it didn't last long. As I write, there are only 140 cattle, 400 pigs, and two donkeys on the place. The average age of the tracors is up to 12 years and, though the overdraft is down to £100 an acre and is only seasonal, the boots are back on. After I finish this I have to go and drag a 100kg dead pig out from the piggery and bury it.

The three men are all gone.

That is my story, but the lads are all the same. Big Hamish and his wife take turns of milking the cows. Mossie has a pigman, but manages his 1000 acres of cereals himself with a boy. Even the Red Rooster, at six foot four with his shock of red hair and surely a man born to give orders rather than execute them, has to work with his hands.

Our newest farmer, whose farm has such a difficult name that he really needs a nickname, is in the most ironical position of all. Ochyoch has 350 acres and no men at all. But worse than that. He is really a crofter in these strange days, for he has a job as a traveller and looks after all that crop in his evenings and weekends.

I suppose Crookie is right when he says: "We are working like hell, but we're nae working class. You canna have half a million pounds worth of farm and call yoursel working class."

Anyway, help is at hand in the form of Mr MacSharry. As far as we can see - and like every other farmer we still cannot see it clearly - he is trying to give us the same money for doing less. That is surely not all bad. We are offended by the thought of the few paternal acres becoming infested with nature against whom our generations have fought, but the thought of the same for less has its attractions.

Mossie is particularly excited by the prospect. "I dinna wint tae be a workin feel," he keeps on saying. He's got his setaside farm bought, and the new acreage payments mean that he won't have to worry so much about sprays and manure for his crops. If you are getting half your money just for showing up you're not going to work so hard at scoring.

And, of course, Mossie is scoring already. He's just built a dual carriageway where his old farm road used to be, and tarred himself the biggest close in Aberdeenshire. It's all to hide the money he's been making. And now he's to get the money without making it.

"It's exciting," he cries, and wonders what he'll do with all his leisure.

He knows what he's going to do next to hide the surplus cash though. It is already commissioned, and before Christmas they'll be unveiling it. Right in the middle of the roundabout in the close at Moss-side - the statue of Lord MacSharry of Setaside.

Bankrupt status symbols

IT WAS on Saturday the first of August at a quarter to nine in the morning. The Breadwinner and I were driving to the Broch, when she shouted out in excitement, "Look, a K." In front of us was a very new and shiny Vauxhall Cavalier.

I'm afraid I was quite unable to share in the excitement as the letters mean nothing to me. In fact we had a K registered Vauxhall about twenty years ago and I thought that was the cause of her excitement. Mind you, I couldn't really see why as that was our first new car and it was a rust covered heap two years later.

So she explained that Saturday was the first day of the new letter. It seemed a remarkable thing that this one should be twenty miles from the seller's garage so early in the morning but apparently that was quite normal. Indeed, some garages opened at midnight to let the proud owners get their new cars.

I find that quite baffling. What possible difference will the letter make? All right you can be the first one seen in a 'K' but it is a short season. By the end of the first week everyone has seen plenty of 'K's. And what's so good about seeing someone else in a fine new car?

I'm glad I haven't got one anyway. It would be such a responsibility having all that newness and having to drive round and round letting everybody see you. And that is what they do. You see plenty of 'K's about but you never see one parked. The Breadwinner and I are having a competition to see who sees a stationary 'K' first and we're both still at a blank. Surely the drivers must soon be exhausted.

I find the whole snobbery of new cars quite bewildering. My idea of motoring is to get something comfortable that can't depreciate more than a thousand pounds a year because that's all it cost. My current one cost a bit more, fifteen hundred in fact but it has lasted three years already and, as far as I can see, it is no

worse than when I got it. There is no way the farm can afford to have me running around in a new car so any such purchase would have to come out of the retirement fundie which isn't doing all that well either.

Of the boys in the discussion group only Big Hamish has bought this year. He's very proud of his 'K' and thinks it stands to reason that that is the car to have. But it's not that Hamish is a car fetishist who is out every day polishing her and bans smoking in case you spoil the upholstery.

It is more that Hamish is a product of the Wasteful Society. He treats his cars like disposable plates or one-trip bottles. He buys a new one, uses it to herd cattle, keep his fencing tools, transport coal and store sweetie papers. In all that Hamish is just like me but when the car finally gives up or when he can't stand it any longer, Hamish goes out and buys a split new one.

It's the same with his house. He finally got fed up with his bungalow just out of earshot of the farm and instead of selling it, he moved into a caravan, knocked the old house down and is building himself a smart new one from scratch. That takes guts, and money. Luckily, even after a year of the best efforts of Weight Watchers and the Clydesdale Bank, he still has plenty of both.

And anyway, we've received news from the South that puts a 'K reg' quite out of the question. According to our information the slump among the fat cats of the City of London is such that there are fantastic bargains to be had in the second-hand markets. Porches, Mercedes and Lamborghinis are being sold for half their book prices, or less.

This is just too much for Mossie. Not content with tarring a couple of acres at Moss-side, and the expense of the statue of MacSharry, he is organising a trip to London to the great car steal. We're going to fly down and drive back in our fleet of bankrupt status symbols.

I'm going along too, but only to observe and to report to you. Mind you, if there is a really smart example of one of the smaller Jaguars I might be tempted, depending on how the harvest turns out.

And the signs there are good. Last Sunday we cut the 27 acres of our winter barley, and the yield was good. I cannot say how good because it has not yet been weighed, and these estimates based on the number of cartloads are just a vehicle for wishful thinking.

I have a neighbour who told us last year, with wonder in his voice, that he had averaged 33.4 hundredweight of rape to the acre.

"Well we had 96 loads." And that was the basis of an estimate to one decimal place. I have a much more scientific reason for optimism. The last time we had winter barley in the second of the fields, the combine cut right round on one fill. So I waited at the gate for the combine to come right round to me.

But this year it stopped when no more than three-quarters of the way round. At first I thought he had stuck, but imagine my joy when the flasher went on and the chute which unloads the combine into the cart came swinging out.

The crop two years ago was near enough to three tonnes, so this year's is more than three tonnes. It is at 17 percent moisture, which will eliminate drying charges - and there is no co-responsibility levy this year.

If the harvest continues like this, I will be driving up the M1 in something a bit special.

Six Jersey cows go on strike

IT HAS been a tiring week. A lot has been happening and I have to report that, for once, most of it was good. The cash flow has been positive and the hope that I will be bringing something a bit special back from the great London car auction SCAM is growing.

First I parted company with six of my last seven Jersey cows. You will remember that I had a great experiment in which I would defy nature by transplanting beefy embryos into these economical little milk machines and therefore make a lot of money. You will also know that nature bit back. The scheme was very good when it worked but that was only now and then. Fertility was the main problem and these six dears have finally gone on strike altogether. Having rejected the bull with the bowler hat they have now declined to go in calf to the real thing, so they are off to Thainstone.

I was sad to see them go. They are lovely cattle to look at and, as I got the hill cow subsidy on them whether they calved or not, they don't owe me any money. But the Black Herefords with which they are to be replaced will also qualify for the subsidy and, as they cost only fifty six pounds a head as calves, they look a better bet.

The last word on the Jerseys is that they averaged £265 against a buying bill of around £300. I hope Reading University who have taken up my experiment make a better job than I did.

The other good news for that saint of a man, my banker (It's all right, he can't read unless you set it out as a balance sheet) is that we sent 83 pigs off to market. I was really very glad to see them go. They have been here far too long and must have lost a lot of money. How much I'll know soon enough. But in the meantime it sends another £7000 or so flowing uphill.

And then there's the winter barley. How bravely I resisted the temptation (which was great) to blaw about the great yield we had. I have been shown up as a blackguard so often in the past by measuring yields through rosy glasses, that I preferred to wait till I could tell you a lie I could stick to.

Well the twenty-seven acres yielded ninety-three tonnes. That is three tonnes nine and the moisture was between 16.4 and 15 percent. Our co-op managed to get me an average of £119 a tonne last year so if they can do that again this year that will be £409 an acre, and remember, there is no levy this year.

Who said winter barley was finished?

It is early days yet. The boys with the broken down driers and those with the heaviest crops are not in yet but I am in the lead. I'm like the leader in the clubhouse with a round of two under par with the leaders still to come. Three tonnes and nine still stands in all the watering holes for ten miles round. So, as you can imagine, I have had a tiring few days. It is no use being in the lead unless you make an appearance. So I have felt it necessary to be in attendance at the various discussion societies every night and even at the jolly lunchtime sessions which are not so common or so dangerous as they were in my fa-ther's time.

I would have to say that Mossie has been a bit annoying over this achievement. As my honorary consultant you might have expected him to stand modestly back and let his part in my success emerge casually. But no chance at all.

He is often heard before he is seen and what he is most often heard to say just now goes a bit like this. "Oh aye, Charlie's in the lead. Three and a half tonnes of Pleasante. Of course it wis me that tell't him fit tae dae. Kept him richt, ye ken." And the really annoying thing is that what he says is true.

I'm glad to say that the Grain Baron is not having things quite all his own way though. I saw him on Saturday night at Sandy Fowlie my cattle buyer's fortieth birthday party. Mossie was there with his mobile barbecue. That's the one he converted from the old rotaspreader. He made the most superb job of the mountainous rib roasts and claims that the wine sauce is the secret. As I ate the succulent and well-hung beef, I reflected once more on what would be if only the average cook knew that beef is not a lump of fresh red stuff.

Now Mossie's wife, a saintly woman, was quite

pleased at the idea of the barbecue. She thought it would be good to have him busily cooking at all the parties and that it would keep him off the other sauce.

Not so. He now has to leave about two hours earlier than anyone else for the parties and finds it essential to taste all the wine that may be accompanying his feasts. Not only that but he gets invited to so many more parties now...no one in Aberdeenshire would think of having a barbecue without having Mossie's Mobile.

And so it was that on Saturday night the great man pleaded with Fiona and I to take him home at midnight to escape the scolding and because he had a batch on the drier that would be just right at midnight.

Unfortunately that was at ten o'clock. By midnight the urge to go home had weakened.

He phoned the next morning to say that the scolding had been great and that it was still going on. He thought maybe the red wine hadn't been very good because he seemed to have a headache. And he was looking for someone to buy barley at 3 percent moisture. The three extra hours in the drier had given him a fine hard sample.

Success of scorched earth policy

We don't burn straw. It is antisocial. It's a waste of straw and of fibre for the soil. No, no. It is far better to use it, sell it, or chop it and plough it down. Mossie doesn't burn straw either but that's only at the weekends when the toonsers might be out driving in the country. They might fuss. "We don't want a scolding," he says.

But we don't burn it ever. Usually.

We had intended to bale all the winter-barley straw for bedding our cattle and pigs through the winter. The twenty-seven acres would give us three hundred bales. It should be less but Big Hamish does the baling and he has twigged that, as he is paid by the bale, the less he puts into them the more money he gets at the end of the day.

In the event there was a bit of a gale. The straw got blown about and we only had two hundred bales. The rest was irretrievably scattered. What was left to do but burn it?

Well, I did everything according to the book. I ploughed carefully round the two fields to make a fire-break. I then went to the far away end and set it going. That meant the fire would burn very slowly because it was progressing up-wind.

It was a slow job at first but help was at hand. The gentle breeze strengthened and then turned through 180 degrees. Soon it was tearing up the field in an angry torrent of flame. It is almost half a mile to the far end but that clearly wasn't going to take long. And at the top, hard up against the steading was my two hundred bales and the hundred and fifty we didn't use last winter. For some reason the ploughman had not made a fire-break in front of the bales.

The only thing to be done was to go up to the steading and start burning from the bales towards the rampant fire and that went very far against the grain. I lit it and then kept it going against the wind with a couple of blan-

88

kets soaked in the horse trough. It was surprisingly easy, as it turned out, and the scorched earth policy did work. When the windblown inferno reached the farm it met the flames which were struggling against the wind, and perished.

When the Breadwinner came home she gave me the scolding for doing anything so wasteful and so dangerous. By that time I was able to tell her that it had all been like a well controlled military operation.

So it was *nearly* a memorable week for that reason, but it *has been* for another.

You will recall that, apart from the Breadwinner and myself, there are the two In-vestments (the girls who stuck in at the school and have careers) and the Wasting Assets (the two boys who left school before they were allowed to, went to the oil and have lived as though there would be no tomorrow. They have been lucky to be proved wrong several times each).

I have to say that the elder of the Wasting Assets has achieved an increase in status. He has borrowed more money than would choke a horse, has bought a restaurant, done up the flat above it, got up before eight every morning and has kept the banker happy for six months. Even more remarkable, he has persuaded his hard-working, charming and accomplished girlfriend to marry him.

For those reasons, and with a great welling-up of parental pride, I have started to refer to John as the Recovery Stock.

But the news is not all good.

When we heard of the marriage we envisaged a trip to Amsterdam, the wedding on a barge and then a week looking at the tulips and windmills.

No chance.

"Everybody gets married on a barge," says this girl who wants to marry the Recovery Stock even if it does mean becoming my daughter-in-law. "I am going to live in Scotland so I want to be married in Scotland."

So we have been busy.

The Salmon Inn has hired a marquee and is attaching that to the bar in which we have our Sunday Discussion Group. Mossie has got the barbecue greased and ready to go and the Butcher has a hundred and fifty pounds of sirloin on-the-bone hanging the necessary three weeks. There's to be smoked salmon and fresh sea trout to start with and the sickliest trifle you ever saw. We're then going to have a ceilidh to show our Dutch guests how odd is our culture. We're then having Scottish country dancing followed by a disco.

It should be fun if only we can iron out the little disagreement about whether there should be alcoholic drink. I can't see the need myself.

Mind you it would have looked bad nipping off to Holland for a week in the middle of harvest. And there is an unexpected side effect of MacSharry which makes it even more important to be ready to pounce when, and only when, the conditions are right.

The price of rape is down from £320 three years ago to about £100. Now, when the price was high it was pretty clear that if the stuff would go through the combine at all we should get on with it. What was £50 a tonne in shrinkage and drying charge when every cwt was worth £16? But now the extra hundredweight is only worth a fiver so we clearly have to get the moisture well down to make harvesting worthwhile at all.

It is a daft situation but with about 60 percent of the return in in subsidies as soon as we have the crop sown, it does make harvesting profitably much more difficult.

Down on hands and knees

EVERY MORNING I rush anxiously out into the field at the east side of of the steading. Down I go on my hands and knees and gently scrape the soil in the hope of finding the delicate shoots of next year's rape crop. You see, I think I have another disaster on my hands.

We got the seeds in only two days after what we consider to be the optimal time and with all the heat that was in the ground we looked for-ward to a quick germination and a firm step towards the harvest of 1993.

But there was a snag. It was day four before I got the pre-emergence herbicidal spray on. I checked that the seeds were indeed pre-emergence and found that though they were chitted the tender shoots were still below the protective cover of Little Ardo's fertile loam. I phoned the Honorary Crops Adviser. "T'hell are you scuttering about at? Get it on. It'll be aa right if it doesna rain." A quick check with the weathermen established that rain was expected any minute. Thus reassured I proceeded to put on the pre-emergence spray.

And then disaster. Despite the experience to the contrary accumulated over many years, the weathermen were correct. Indeed they had maybe under-estimated the downpour both in intensity and in duration. "The herbicide will aa be washed doon intae the grun and aa yer sproots'll be died," said the adviser who hasn't forgiven me for getting a bigger crop of winter barley than him. "But fit dis it matter? You'll get enough plants to qualify for the acreage payment which is mair than the stuff's worth onyway."

It's true but that doesn't mean I am enjoying the prospect of a disaster.

This year's crop on the other hand is good. We had an average of 28.5 hundredweights. The Tapidor again had sclerotinia which reduced its yield quite a bit but the Falcon was just great. I think there may have been just over a tonne of Tapidor and perhaps 32 hundredweights of Falcon though, as it all goes into one heap, I can't really say.

So how has MacSharry affected me so far? With last year's arrangements and price of £225 a tonne I would have got an average of £312 an acre but with MacSharry and £110 a tonne I should be £22 an acre better off.

But the hard thing to get used to is the way MacSharry encourages you to make a mess of things. With my good crop of Falcon I am £9 worse off. All the benefit comes from the bad crop of Tapidor. There I am £109 an acre better off than I'd have been under the old regime.

Of course that is what MacSharry wants - inefficiency. And that is difficult for us farmers to grasp. But we're quick learners and I look forward with some unease to what will happen to our farming skills, so long acquired, when MacSharry is applied to all crops.

Thank goodness we are still on the old system for the wheat. We are still operating the old-fashioned and totally out of date idea that efficiency should be encouraged. And on that score I am optimistic. The wheat is looking well all over the North East and bumper crops are being anticipated provided we can get them harvested.

You see, so heavy are

most people's crops that they are all lying flat except for those that are twisted. Fifty percent lodging is average and some are glad of the tram-lines to give them a little show of standing crop. If the winter comes as early as it is threatening to as I write, a large part of those crops will be left for the pheasants or disappear into the drying bills.

There are however a few fields which are standing and I can tell you that a high pro-portion of them are at Moss-side and at Little Ardo.

Now, you know that nei-ther Mossie nor I is the type who would go down to the pub and blaw about how good we were at the farming game, but I decided to make this an exception. I was really look-ing forward to raising the subject at Sunday's discus-sion group.

I waited until we were wearing down the second pint before saying that we seemed to be the only places round about with standing corn. I expected him to take most of the praise but I hoped some-thing might be left for me.

But I was quite unprepared for Mossie's response.

"An absolute disaster. I've never been so humiliated in aa my life. Aabody's crops flat but mine and yours and yours dinna coont. Me the best fairmer in the country and theiy're aa sayin my wheat's too light to lodge. I tell you. I'm gaun tae gang oot the night and tramp some o't doon just to show them."

And I think he must have for I was passing Moss-side yesterday and the field beside the road has a decent show of lodging.

Little Ardo, on the other hand, still hasn't one straw down despite the monsoon which is washing the last of the Butisan down to the sprouts of my next year's rape.

If only it would dry up a bit I'd be away out with the wellies to tramp a bit of the wheat down. The ten acre field that looks down into the village will do nicely. I can't have them thinking that the toil of my forefathers has come to this - the only light crop in the district.

All done up like a dog's dinner

IT WAS the first time I had been to a registry office wedding and I must say I faced the prospect with some trepidation. I had feared something of the atmosphere of a crossing point on the Iron Curtain.

I was favourably surprised. There was enough atmosphere to provoke the odd tear and enough solemnity about the occasion to ensure that the young couple would be impressed by the enormity of what they were taking on.

I remembered the day when one of my university friends got married in a registry office. It is said that he had his leather jacket polished for the occasion but had made no other concession to the occasion.

But we were done up like proper dogs' dinners. The Recovery Stock was resplendent in his kilt and Prince Charlie jacket as was I. And so too was the Best Man - and the Wasting Asset looked scrubbed and like butter wouldn't melt in his mouth.

The Breadwinner was turned out a treat in a bit of Belgian lace her mother had bought in Brussels before the war and the Investments were looking like investments should when the family is exposing its best face to the world.

Having invited our friends to a ceilidh to celebrate the marriage we then found ourselves ridiculously over-dressed for the evening as our guests turned up in sweaters and jeans - but it didn't matter.

The ceilidh was really an economy measure. Instead of a band we would make do with what our friends could do.

Now one of those is John Pratt the son of Sandy Pratt who you may well know from all the times he has proposed the direct negative at meetings of the National Farmers' Union of Scotland. John plays the pipes and had been warned that his wedding present was to be "a tuney".

I phoned him on the morning of the 'do' to make sure that he brought his pipes. "If

it's a fine night you could be standing at the door and pipe them in. Then after they've had time for a maximum of two glasses of my champagne I'll ask them all to sit down and you could pipe them in. Then you could maybe play for the Grand March and after that maybe you could give us an eightsome reel?"

John listened stoically to the lengthening list and then said with no more than a hint of a smile, "You wouldna like me to lift a twenty acre o' rape while I'm at it would you?"

That is a remark which I will never forget. It is a perfect example of the idiom which marks out where I live as somewhere a little different and a little special.

The groom's speech also departed somewhat from tradition. He shocked them all by omitting "My wife and I..." and substituting "As Dani's husband..." which I thought was very in tune with these days of women's rights. He not only thanked his in-laws for the hand of their daughter but thanked me for his promotion to Recovery Stock. He beat me to the joke that I was not so much losing a Wasting Asset as gaining an Investment. He then reaffirmed his marriage vows for the benefit of those who weren't at the registry office.

And then he did something that had even the Farmer grabbing for the handkerchief. He apologised to his mother for having been such a difficult child.

That was a most touching moment but by no means inappropriate.

After such a noble gesture I should perhaps have refrained from telling the company about when we were living in Dundee and John went missing. I searched the notorious Dichtie burn with a heavy heart, searching for what I could not bear to find.

After a frantic hour or so I saw two little figures holding hands and each with a hammer in the free hand. It was John aged two and Mark aged four. "Hello boys, where have you been?"

"There were lots of lorries," said John excitedly.

With the care that age brings the four year old added, "And all the windows were broken when we got there."

So were the reflectors, the lights, the indicators and the mirrors.

I stood amid the devastation with the owner of the five lorries, as he said "Good God. Good God." Then he took a sharp breath, looked at me, guessed that we were talking about a year's pay here and said, "Well it's only bairns." He then took stock of the weather. "It's a right fine day," he said and went back into the house.

That story didn't spoil the wedding, though it was already spoiled for Mossie. He had chosen, hung and cooked a hundredweight and a quarter of rib roast to perfection only to have to serve it over an hour late. "Underdone madam? No sorry. We have it well done or cremated." The Red Rooster, who had been looking very snappy, was helping with the carving and somehow managed to get about a pint of fat down the front of his kilt. And Big Hamish couldn't get a fight anywhere.

There was only one thing that worried me. Everybody kept coming up and telling me how pretty the younger Investment was looking and how it would be her next. Well, I am not keen on giving my Investments away at the best of times, and especially not now that I have had an update on the price of champagne.

My guns are arrested by the local bobby

I HAD a dramatic illustration this week of the fact that less and less labour is needed on the farms. You may well be fed up of me telling you that, with rather fewer acres, my father ran Little Ardo with a staff of six. Despite that, he enjoyed the life of a gentleman and an income which was well above average.

I, on the other hand, am a working crofter on my 250 acres and my income is usually well below the figures published as average for the country. I have to rely on the Breadwinner to pay for the holidays and the insurance policies against the possibility that we may have an old age.

There are no men now unless you count the Wasting Asset, who can sometimes spare an hour or two between getting up and dressing to "Ging oot", and Potions the local chemist who is a frustrated farmer and nips down sometimes to play at mucking-out.

It's partly because we've cut some corners which never should have been there in the first place. It is many years since we saw that the stots would go fat just as quick even if we neglected to plat their tails on Saturday nights. They don't look as well on Sunday but there has been no discernable impact on the conversion rate.

But the change has mostly been brought about by mechanisation. We had a good illustration of that this week when we were making silage.

Now, the innovation in silage-making in the last ten years has been the advent of the big bale. That saves labour in all sorts of ways and I like it particularly because I can set one bale down opposite a small pen of animals and that is them fed for as much as a week.

Four years ago we decided to go for the big bales and would employ a tubeliner. We had no idea of what we were doing and neither had the contractor. It took us four days to wrap two hundred and fifty bales. We had two balers, two bringing the bales home, one loading the wrapper, one operating the wrapper and one moving the wrapper. The squad was seven, the language was blue and it cost us over six pounds a bale to do the job.

Last year we went onto individual bales and the squad was two balers, two bringing home and loading the wrapper, one wrapper operator and one unloading and stacking. The squad was down to six.

This year the squad was down to just three. One baler, one bringing home and one miracle-worker who loaded, operated the wrapper, and stacked.

I have a new (that is to say not nearly as old) torque digger which helps the bringing home but the breakthrough is in the wrapping. The one man loads the wrapper and then points a remote control thing at it - it is just like we use to change channels on the telly and while he stacks the previous bale the wrapper gets on with the wrapping. That way the whole lot were baled in a leisurely afternoon and at a cost of nearer four pounds a bale. Half the men have been

banished from the silage field in one year.

I am not happy about the depopulation of the farms but I am happy about the cost cutting. I am also pleased because despite the floods we managed to get one really good drying day. It would have been much better with another drying day but it poured all the next day. It proved once again the old adage that the time to shoot a rabbit is when you see it.

I have been resisting the temptation to shoot the wheat though. There is still a greenness about it and as it is still all standing I feel justified in holding off, though it is a test of nerve. And next year's rape is peeping coyly through the ground raising hopes that, despite my tardy application of the pre-emergence weedkiller, all may be well.

However last week was not a simple case of one triumph after another. My guns have been arrested. When I came back from Africa I was determined to be better about the laws of the land and I decided to licence grandpa's old gun which lay in the loft and which I intended to use to scare the doos off the rape.

That was done and I have scared doos legally for three years. But then my licence ran out. I got a friendly phone call from the local Bobby and set about renewing my licence. It proved almost as difficult for me as applying for the rape subsidy. Getting four identical photos, getting them signed by a JP, and getting the form filled up and down to the station altogether seemed very difficult. When I did manage it I had no cheque book.

So, by the time I had done the deed the licence was out of date and I was in breach of the firearms laws.

And so it was that three police arrived at Little Ardo to confiscate my guns. They were quite nice about it. They were led by a young man who had started shaving and he was followed by two pretty little girls who had presumably left school already. I didn't get a receipt for the guns but I wasn't worried. I hardly ever use them.

But I do miss them. Have you noticed how pheasants seem to know when February has come, bringing the end of the shooting season? Then they strut about all over the place though when you had a few friends in for a bit of rough shooting there was not a bird to be seen.

Well, it was just like that when they confiscated my guns. Suddenly the garden is overrun with rabbits. The Breadwinner is not amused and there is nothing I can do about it.

99

Not easy to retreat with good grace

YOU'VE HEARD me say it before but I must say it again today. The biggest crop of oats I have ever heard of was at the Pitfour Arms at Mintlaw about half-past-ten one Saturday night.

Well, that may be true of oats, but the record for wheat may be beaten at the Salmon Inn, for we have the most wonderful cascade of golden berries. We have two and a wee bit fields cut out of the four and we have 95 tonnes away to the grain store at between 20 and 26% moisture. There are still about twenty tonnes to go. In which case we will have four tonnes to the acre unless the twenty tonnes turns out to be less or the 'wee bit' of the park turns out to be a bigger bit than we thought.

It is so difficult to be sure that one is not blawin in vain. Anyway my three and a half tonnes of winter barley is still in the lead and I am well enough pleased with a tonne and a half of winter rape. That is up three quarters of a tonne and half a tonne respectively, on last year and, with the benefits of MacSharry, it is clear that I am going to have a problem of knowing what to do with all the money.

Mind you, winning the wheat has been an embarrassing business.

First there was the fuss that I made about the contractor cutting the first park across the brae.

You may recall that two years ago they did that and couped a cartful of grain when they were loading it. I will never get over the job of trying to recover the four tonnes of wheat from the stubble. And there was worse to come. In no time at all the field was adorned with luxuriant green stripes where all the grain that had spilled over the low side of the riddles had landed.

I told the contractor then that if he did that again he needn't come back and he, raised himself, blamed me for telling him to cut across the tramlines.

So you can imagine my wrath as I discovered that they were again going across

the park on the brae, in full view of the village. By the time I was pulling open the door of the cab I was fifteen feet off the ground and rising. "T'hell de ye think ye're daein? I dinna suppose ye've got self-levelling riddles."

He explained that the park was just too steep and the combine wouldn't climb her so there was no alternative.

"C'mon an see this," says I and jumped down.

But search as I might I could find no more than a very few spilled grains. The lad had been crawling along and hadn't spilt much at all. When you've been as high as I had been it isn't easy to come down again with a good

grace and, I'm ashamed to say, I didn't really try as hard as I might have.

Certainly not as hard as I would have, had I known how the rest of the day would go.

Now, MacSharry may be a good thing for farmers about here though it is a disaster for employed men on the farm, but it is also potentially very bad for the contractors. There will be much less work about. So the contractors are distinctly jumpy anyway. And the way to make them really mad is to hold them up in the harvest field.

So you can imagine how much we all enjoyed the burst wheel we had when we had moved to the farthest away field of wheat on the place. It was a back wheel and we had five tonnes of wheat on it. So I would run home for the old International. There were signs of impatience by the time I returned with the old dear blowing reek out of her like a Prairie Queen from the old Wild West.

She doesn't have a pick-up hitch and we had no jack at all in the field and no decent jack that would do the job with five tonnes of barley in the cart on soft ground. So with steam starting to come out of the combine I ran (if so you can describe my agitated arthritic hobbling these days) the half mile back to the steading for the digger. I had just got her on the road to the field when a lorry came in about for a load of grain, as though I wasn't embarrassed enough already.

Eventually we got the old girl yoked and the load home but by that time the combine was full again and waiting as she strove in first gear with the five tonnes.

The digger and I arrived in the close just in time to stop the lorry leaving with an empty cart. The Wasting Asset took the old International back to the field. He got the combine emptied just before the old International died.

"Oh, for God's sake," said the combine driver who was now about eight feet tall and very strong and angry looking, "Go to Wardies and get my tractor or we'll never be finished. It's an International and you'll find it in the close."

The Wasting Asset took me the two miles to Wardies but when we got there the only tractor we could see was a Case. In my fluster of stopping the combine it took a good ten minutes of dithering before I remembered that that was the name of the company that took over the Internationals.

All was well thereafter but the damage had been done. Any lead I had over the contractor as a result of him cutting across the park was dissipated. By the time he got to his next job he found someone else in the park.

And he wasn't the only one who lost money out of the deal. Apart from the repairs to my two antique tractors I am to lose out more. Big Hamish is needing an extra twenty pence a bale for the brae park because of the discomfort of baling across the tramlines.

That is the bad news. The good news is that we have about four tonnes so far and the very best park is still to come.

September 28, 1992

Wheeling & dealing for new digger

THE HARVEST drags on and continues to look good. Inevitably though, it doesn't look quite as good as I expected. You will remember that last week I was dreaming of the four tonne crop of wheat. Well, I fear I was only dreaming right enough. The absolutely best park which we had left till last because it was all standing and might still be filling, turned out to be the worst and spoiled the average it was supposed to push over the four tonnes. And that was after all the lies I told the boys about the weight of this year's crop.

Still it will be good, and, with the market looking strong, I have been lashing out the money. I have upgraded the old digger. I was sad to see her go, but I had had too many soakings feeding cattle in winter with no protection from the wind which can blow from the North Pole to Little Ardo without an interuption. There is hardly a tree and not one hill to the north of us here, on the edge of Buchan.

Now there is among the lads who meet at the Salmon on a Sunday to discuss the state of the country and our neighbours' crops, one of the army of people forced off the land and into gainful employment by these changing times. His people farmed in Orkney and saw that if they could win at all there the job would be a dawdle on Aberdeenshire's fertile acres.

So it was, but Magnus saw that there were easier ways to make a living than working and became a dealer specialising in anything that was cheap and could be made to look dear. We call him Mr Fifteen Percent because that is a generous estimate of what he takes on his deals.

He is worth it. He serves the industry well and, if he serves himself well at the same time, we shouldn't complain. And it is not just me that he has served on this occasion.

As far as I can understand it, Fifteen Percent worked the latest deal like this. He sold a new digger to a white settler

103

who is just beginning to get rid of his fortune, for twenty-nine thousand pounds. But in order to clinch the deal he had to take the last digger he had sold him, back for fourteen. He then sold that one to another farmer for sixteen but had to take his old digger back for five thousand. He sold that to another farmer for six but had to take his digger as a trade-in for two thousand eight hundred. He was thus able to give me this wonderful bargain of a great new old digger for three thousand four hundred. He took my old cabless wreck for fifteen hundred and an extra three hundred for the back acter. My Coburn track just couldn't stand the back acter

any more.

So now I have a digger, which I suppose should be called an industrial loader, as the back acter is away. It starts in the morning, has torque (which means, as far as I can see, that it has only two gears...forward and back), has a watertight cab, a seat, an indicator for showing that you are going to turn right, an offside side light and a quite inopperable handbrake.

This represents a considerable upgrading of my plant and I am very happy about it. My loader is down from twenty-two years old to no more than eleven. It's a pity the children aren't young any more. They would have been

so proud.

So you see Mr Fifteen Percent has been busy and has had a lot of percents out of the deal. But the one that intrigues me is the one in which he disposed of my old digger. How did he manage to get his fifteen percent out of that and stay out of jail? I suppose if I knew the answer to that one I too would be rich.

We have got the winter barley in now, just in time. We reckon it must be in by the twenty-first of September and we made that with two days to spare. Many farmers have said that they are stopping that crop as part of their response to setaside. But I can't really do that after leading the field with my three and a half tonnes this year. I've dressed out some of my own seed and am looking for the same again next year.

Besides I'm not even sure that I will reduce my cereal acreage in response to setaside. There is a furious debate going on as to what we should do and I still haven't made up my mind. In fact I don't really understand what it is I can or can't do.

Mossie says that his hero MacSharry has sent us another ideal break crop. If we take the setaside money and use the green cover to set up a good wheat in the following year, we'll get an extra half tonne to the acre.

He may be right but I am thrawn. Currently my favourite plan is to plough up my silage grass for wheat. Sow a late maturing grass in my setaside, top it in the spring, and make bad silage of it on the fifteenth of July. They won't let me manure my setaside, which is a pity, but it is said that I can slurry it which would be just as effective if I can get the timing right.

It is not easy. How I ache for the days when it was the job of the farmer to make two stems of grass grow where only one grew before. I am not happy with a regime that asks me to make one grow where two grew before, and, try as they may, they won't make me feel bad about trying to beat the system. I am only trying to make the best of the bad job they have given me.

Making the best of a ropey job

"All I need is a tall ship and a star to steer her by."

THUS SANG the Wasting Asset as he brought home the last load of wheat. I had had to go off to a long-promised speaking engagement and the lad had agreed to bring home the last few loads. But the nights are drawing in at an alarming rate and by the time the third last load was home everyone else round about had on the lights.

The lights were on the combine but our best tractor, the 590, doesn't have lights. She does of course have sockets and the occasional bulb even, as well as quite a lot of wires but that doesn't amount to a lighting system. So the Asset had to hope he wouldn't meet anyone on the road home. It was almost completely dark by the time he had the second last load and there was not even a lowe

106

on the horizon when he got the last.

It was easy enough when he was unloading the combine for there he had the light of the great mobile thrashing mill to work with. But on the road home he had to take a fix on the moon. He made it home of course but drew the line at tipping her. I saw that the minute I returned. The loaded cart was abandoned at half mast in the middle of the pitch-black close.

Now, it is to the Asset's credit that he made no complaint about the poor state in which he had found his plant. He just shared the Farmer's joy at a harvest won, the clyak sheaf cut and the harvest home. After his short lifetime on Little Ardo he doesn't expect there to be lights on tractors. He thinks well of me because the tractors now have cabs, not to mention power-steering and brakes.

But Mossie is scandalised. "T'Hell are ye daein makin the loon work be the licht o the moon and steerin be the stars?" he shouted at me at the discussion group last Sunday. "That's a disgrace and look at aa the money you're makin. Spend some o't."

It's all right for him, a Grain Baron and member of the thousand acre club. But with my record as a cereal grower, and with all those damned cattle to support over the years, the secret of my survival has been low overheads. There is no other way, short of being a genius, for the crofter. And that is what I am these days. Little Ardo once sent a dozen bairns for schooling and six wives for shopping in the village. Now it only has half a job for the Farmer.

So the Farmer appreciated the Asset's attitude of making the best of a pretty ropey job.

It was in contrast to the next generation at Moss-side. They expect the best, which is just as it should be, but they don't feel they are getting it.

Unlike me, Mossie's credibility as a farmer is such that he need never be without the very best of machinery. All he has to do is to ask the distributors for a demonstration and that way he can have the best without even paying for it. Sometimes they forget about their demonstration models for ages. Their idea is that he will be shamed into a purchase because he has had the demonstration for so long. But there is no shame in him.

Well now, Mossie is a great pro-European thanks to the good things he reckons MacSharry has done for us, and has an exotic fleet of huge tractors from Italy. I'm most impressed but not so the next generation at Moss-side. Young Mossie wants a big Ford. I visited the other day to find the boy in a sombre mood. "The hankies are oot," he says, "the new Ford's awa back." He then proceeded to tell me about all the comforts, not to mention agricultural advantages he was foregoing in returning to the 'old' tractors.

It meant nothing to the Farmer who lives in another world but it did give me defence against Mossie's abuse of me for not having lights. "What a shame," I was able to say, "Making poor Young Mossie drive these two-year-old tractors when for a mere thirty grand he could have been working in real comfort."

Anyway, old tractors by moonlight may have been the way it finished but the wheatfield was left with honour. The fifty-five acres has yielded three tonnes and fourteen hundredweights per acre which is my best ever. At that we are close to five hundred pounds an acre and the ground itself isn't worth much more than that. We'll surely manage.

In fact we think we have the perfect rotation now. Winter wheat, spring rape and back to wheat.

Mind you there are two snags. The first is that the rape is still lying sodden in the fields. That doesn't matter for all we will lose if we can't harvest it - surely after drying charges and the cost of the combine it can't leave us more than fifty pounds an acre and it is likely to be less. MacSharry means we have already earned most of the harvest in acreage payment. No, the trouble just might be that we can't get the fields cleared in time to get the wheat in to advantage.

And the other snag with the new rotation is that we have to set it aside every six years and there is going to be little profit in that - and no joy.

Twenty-six mamas roar in the night

"There was a roaring in the woods all night.
The rain came dashing down and fell in floods."

THAT RHYMELESS couplet, which I think may be from Wordsworth and is almost certainly wrong, was in my head all last night. It seemed to sum up my farming scene as I lay there unable to sleep.

It was not the fifty-two acres of spring rape which has now been swathed for four weeks and is beginning to sprout, that kept me awake. That really doesn't matter any more thanks to MacSharry's reforms. We've already had two thirds of our money through the new grant system so if we never get a harvest we will save as much in combining and drying charges as the stuff will be worth.

And it's not the overdraft. It is down to the sort of money Mossie and the Red Rooster would spend on a car for the wife.

No it was the roaring that kept me awake. We decided to wean our calves though there was still three weeks of the grazing season still to go. It was really Potions, the chemist who is a source of zero-cost labour at Little Ardo, who wanted to get the calves in.

He has been engaged in improvements. He has removed the last remnants of the traivises and troughs from the old dairy byre. That will be a great blessing when it comes to mucking-out next and he was anxious to bring that day nearer by starting to make muck in it.

I was not so keen as I had been enjoying the fact that God was feeding the cattle and I wasn't looking forward to starting the daily grind of winter feeding. It seemed early to be weaning them too as they are mostly late spring calves. Anyway, I was persuaded that they would be better onto some feed and that the cows and the in-calf heifers would eat up every morsel of grass that was left.

We weaned twenty bull calves and seven heifer calves from the twenty six cows. "That is tremendous," I hear you say. Well, I am quite pleased but I have to remind you of the six yeld Jerseys that went away to the jingoring.

The best April calf is a Belgian Blue cross weighing six hundredweights and with a backside like a Sumo wrestler, but the champion is a set of pure Simmental twin bulls born in December. That cow is owe me nothing for she has raised fourteen hundredweights of beef this summer.

So there has been a roaring in the woods all night as twenty-six mamas, who should be glad of the rest, roar for their calves and the calves roar back for their milk.

I must be very hard-hearted but my main feeling about all that trauma is my worry that our barriers won't be strong enough to keep the calves in or that the fences won't be much use against the determined cows. As the dawn breaks this morning and the dawn chorus has a deeper note than usual, I have seen no sign yet of my principal fear. They have not been looking for one another on the lawn or in the Breadwinner's flowerbeds.

As I write there have been three weeks in which the combines have been silent. The harvest which had gone so well has ground squelching to a halt. Day after day the heavens have opened and poured forth.

One farmer is said to have a thousand acres to cut. If he had got it right that would have sold this year for half a million so it can't be helping his cash flow. Perhaps he has got too big.

But it's not just the big boys who have problems. I have a neighbour who has three small fields of wheat which look as though they have been levelled by a road roller. Not even the tramlines are standing. That has been flat for six weeks. I suppose it was cheeky of me but I stopped and had a wander about in one of those fields the other day.

It was a most depressing experience. The heads which are off the ground are alright but how is he ever to harvest them? All the heads which are on the ground are sprouting fast. That is producing a mat of roots and shoots and rotting straw which I can't imagine ever being dry enough to let the savable seeds go through the combine.

Big Hamish has still four

hundred acres of rape to lift and is investigating whether he can get tracks put on his combine or even floats for three hundred acres he has taken in a swamp which used to be down by the sea and now appears to be in it. I think his only hope is the snipe shooting

The Red Rooster has wheat, rape and linseed lying and he can't wait for the MacSharry system to be extended to cover cereals.

It's serious. There will be bankruptcies for sure. People have been leaving the land at between one and two percent since the war. The latest figures are nearer four percent and this won't help.

I was discussing all this with Mossie, the Grain Baron, the other day. He's alright of course because, like me, he's only got MacSharry crops lying. That didn't stop us shaking our heads about the weather though. I had seen the forecast and was trying to look on the bright side.

"They say there's to be bright intervals," says I.

"Aye," says Mossie, "that'll be the lightning."

Rats carry a peculiar menace

THE STOCKING rate has reached its highest for many years and perhaps it is at an all time high. And yet I am not happy about it. You see it is caused by an invasion of rats.

When I was a boy I remember that there were always rats about the place. Any summer evening, if you looked out of the kitchen window, you could see them bouncing menacingly across the close. And there was a sort of ratting motorway between the old pump house and the barn where they scuttled back and forth all day.

We had excellent cats, half a dozen or so, which lived well on the young rats and the grieve had a keen little terrier with which we hunted rats for our pleasure and for the good of the farm.

The best sport was at thrashing time when we separated the straw from the grain, the feed from the bedding. That meant taking down the rucks which were homes to hundreds of rats in winter.

As we took the rucks down the rats moved down so that the concentration of rodents grew greater and greater. The last hundred sheaves or so could displace a hundred rats or more. As the last sheaves were removed we all gathered round, a murderous crew with shovels, forks and spades and the terrier waiting to pounce.

On one such occasion, my father was watching but was not taking an active part. There was a breakout at the far side of the ruck and we all dashed round to batter them. But when we left the rats took the opportunity to make a break for it past the lone figure of my father. When we came round he had a rat under each foot and was scrabbling for others with his bare hands.

Those were not the days.

In recent years there has been nothing like that at Little Ardo. In fact for many years after the advent of warfarin there were few or even no rats here. The occasional sighting was dealt with by putting down tracking powder.

I think four things have

gone wrong. First we have started to keep pigs again and it is not possible to feed the pigs in a way that starves the rats. Second, you can't get rats to take bait when there is tasty feed around, thirdly they have become immune to tracking powder and fourth the attempts to poison the rats have led to the secondary poisoning of the cats. If the rats have some tracking powder in them it is bad for the cats. Certainly we have no cats left here.

This was all brought to a head when we took the calves in last week.

I got a load of cake for them in bulk and bagged it off into the plastic bags in which they used to deliver our seed grains. In the bottom shed we dumped a tonne of this stuff.

The next morning I noticed a few holes appearing in the side of the bags. The day after that there were considerable rents all round the bags and quite a lot spilled on the floor. The third day it was a shambles. It looked just like it does when you have a cattle beast gets loose and excited.

And yet there was no cattle dung so it couldn't be a cow. There was very little fouling so I thought it couldn't be rats. Anyway the devastation was far beyond what rats could do. How

could rats pull hundred-weight sacks right over?

Everyone made a trip to see this phenomenon. The Breadwinner said it might be badgers, which was a pretty thought except that there has never been a known badger here. Potions hates rats so he hoped it was a fox, though nothing less than a pack of them could have made such a mess. Mossie said "T'hell difference dis it mak what it is. Get it up oot o' that afore its aa eaten." But the spirit of scientific enquiry wouldn't let me do that. That night I left the light on in the shed. As I stole down the close I could hear the tearing of the bags as something huge ripped and gnawed at my profit margin. The badger theory started to look good. I climbed up onto the ramp we use to load our pigs and peered through the Yorkshire boarding.

And there they were. The mystery was no mystery. It was just rats and rats and rats. A hideous grey carpet covered the nuts.

I would shoot them. I could have got ever so many with my two barrels and that just might have been a lesson to them and encouraged them to move off to another farm.

But then I remembered that my guns had been

arrested because my licence was out of date. I've renewed it but they still haven't brought my guns back.

So I left them to it and went off round to the Salmon course I didn't like losing a hundred pounds worth of cattle feed but it was more than that. The rat may be a very intelligent mammal, and it may be a long time since it

for a beer with the boys. I know they found me unusually silent and the beer had a queer metallic after-taste. Of brought the black death, but they still carry a peculiar menace and in numbers give a unique horror.

Crookie takes the plunge

FARMING FAIRLY took a back seat this week. For, after nearly forty years of being a batchelor, Crookie finally got wed.

And what a do it was. It was the sort of event that makes the ignorant city dwellers think all farmers are rich. Certainly, if the bride's father is rich after that wedding he must indeed have been blessed before it.

As you would expect when two farming families meet for an alliance, it was held in the Cathedral. And it is the first wedding I've been to where the numbers were restricted by the size of the church. Big Hamish was about the only person of importance in the county who wasn't there but there just wouldn't have been a seat.

Eric Stephen, the Union man, raised the interesting question as to how many acres there were represented at the do - not counting hills. So I set about a rough count and came up with a figure of a hundred thousand arable acres.

Some wedding this. But Mossie, who was very impressed with the figure, capped it. "Aye, but how many millions of overdraft are there at this wedding?" I couldn't have begun a count there but there was at least one overdraft millionaire and several candidates.

So it was a glittering occasion and I was rather touched by one aspect of my friend's behaviour as he waited patiently in the church to go through that door which I went through those thirty-odd years ago.

Most grooms stand like stuckies at the altar, frozen in their batchelorhood as the bridal march rings out and a tearful father leads his terrified daughter to meet her match. The first the groom sees of his wife-to-be is a sideways glance when she comes up to him.

But not Crookie. When the great fanfare sounded he turned full round, and as though in wonder that she had indeed turned up, enjoyed with the rest of us the full glory of his bride's triumphant entrance. He must have been pleased with what he saw for she is a looker at any time but on her wedding day Fiona looked quite stunning.

It was not always so. She looks no better than average when she has been drenched from top to toes in many gallons of magnesium syrup laced with sheep dip, harled with sand and top dressed with half a hundredweight of feathers.

You may well be wondering how I would know that. I know it because I have seen it.

There is an old pre-nuptial custom in Aberdeenshire that the young man's friends wash his feet for him to make sure that he comes clean to the matrimonial bed. There is no doubt that in the days before saunas, jaccuzzis or even the tap at the back door, the tradition was a useful one. But nowadays feet are kept so clean that there is no fun in washing them.

Indeed, the custom has become so corrupted that the object is to make, not only his feet, but the whole groom as dirty as possible, while doing their best to promote the shares in Scottish and Newcastle breweries.

And so it was that they caught Crookie three weeks before the wedding and set upon him with the bursen oil, the mag. syrup and the sheep dip. He put up a good show but lost the fight and most of his clothes. With so much sticky stuff about, the loss of the clothes was a distinct advantage but the shoes were a severe loss for the underfoot conditions favoured the well-shod. They hopped in with another salvo of unpleasant garnish for our man while he did his best to retaliate in a way that reminded me of a stot that had had too much barley and was a bit hot among its feet.

Now you may be wondering why on earth a man of my maturity, not to say years, would put himself within pouring distance of such an event.

Well, much as I desired to see my friend well married, I would not have gone to the feet-washing for all the acres that there were at the wedding. I am able to report all this to you because of one of the horrors of the technological revolution. The whole do was video-taped, up to the point at which the camera woman and her camera suffered total immersion in treacle.

But that wasn't before the lovely bride ventured too close to her tormented lover

116

and got sprayed, soaked and finally drookit, £9 hairdo, clothes and all, in treacle - a whole pailful for the hairdo. Then came the feathers and the sand. Even at that she was a handsome woman so it was no surprise that Crookie's eyes shone when he looked round and saw her coming up the aisle at him in St. Machar's Cathedral.

It's been a bit of an assault course for there was also a stag night. Luckily I was away on holiday so I missed it but apparently it was a most jolly occasion. It was scheduled for Monday but also took in a sizeable slice of Tuesday.

So poor Crookie has entered a whole new estate. And he could hardly have done so at a worse time. He has ninety acres of tatties still in the ground and a lucrative contract to supply them to the Russians beckoning. And yet the new wife, not a day after their marriage, is insisting on the poor man going away on, of all things, a holiday. A holiday with ninety acres of tatties in the ground? It's unthinkable.

Frankly, we're worried about our friend. We had a good session on it at the discussion group on Sunday evening. You see, if he lets the wife get right on top of him for a start like that, what hope is there for him?

Mossie's going to speak

to him when he gets back. "Jist tell her, there's tae be nae mair holidays when there's tatties in the grun. And mak a point o comin to the discussion group on Sunday or you'll maybe never get oot again."

Enough's enough of abuse

I HAVE to confess to the worst harvest crime of all.

"Now what would that be?" I hear you ask.

When I was a boy it was setting a sheaf down arse for elbow so that the builder had to turn it round before placing it on the stack. It was important to the timeless toil of leading home the crop that the rhythm of the work was kept up and the forker became, as he had to be, won-

derfully skilled at landing each sheaf at exactly the right place so that it could be placed with the minimum of labour. A good forker could almost build the ruck himself so accurate was he as he tossed the sheaves from the cart to the stack.

There were tensions though. Old Jimmy Low, the grieve for forty six years at Little Ardo, used to build the rucks and he grew very tense indeed if a sheaf should land six inches out of place and if it should land the wrong way round - well, look out.

I remember watching in wonder as the great task was accomplished in the late forties. It had been a slow season and tempers were getting short anyway. For a reason which I could not fathom, the grieve was not satisfied with the way the sheaves were coming at him. The forker wasn't too pleased with the coaching he was getting either.

Now there is a tricky bit for the forker when the builder is at the far side of the ruck. As he works his way round, there comes a time when he turns and instead of the sheaf landing to his left he expects it on his right hand. It is easy to get the first sheaf on the other hand a little bit out of place. Whether it was by accident or design I will never know but, as Jimmy turned to receive the first sheaf on his right hand, he was caught full in the face with the stubble end of the sheaf.

A saint would not have been amused and, though I can't be sure of what he's doing now, Jimmy was no saint in those days. His face painfully scratched, he sprang as one possessed from the ruck to the cart, got on top of the forker and gave him a few hefty dunts on the face. He then returned to the ruck and the work resumed with good grace on both sides.

My most serious harvest crime in those days was to take my foot too swiftly off the clutch when driving the tractor between the stooks and almost knocking the foreman who was building it off the cart. I was a runner of professional standard in those days so I was in no great danger, and again the chase seemed to clear the air.

Those harvest crimes were serious but they were nothing to what I did on the last day of lifting the rape this year.

For many reasons, into which I shall not go meantime, I was tired. The contractor was tired too. He had been rushing around like a headless chicken trying to keep me and his many other clients happy through weather in which no farmer could be happy.

Now, you will appreciate that driving the cart that keeps the combine emptied, is not an exacting job with rape unless you are several miles from the steading and we were only two small fields away. The excitement of keeping up was not sufficient and I twice fell asleep at the wheel as I waited.

So the next time I was home with a load I decided to leave the cart inside the first field and nip in to the house for a quick cup of coffee. Maybe that would wake me up.

It fairly didn't. Indeed I only got a couple of sips in before I fell fast asleep.

You can imagine my horror when I woke up quarter of an hour later. I would have committed the greatest crime of all. I would have stopped the combine. Out I rushed to see the great machine come charging up through the field of newly sown winter rape. He swung round at the cart and started discharging all round it.

Now, old Jimmy Low would undoubtedly have come down off the combine, given me a good thrashing and in five minutes it would all have been over. But that is not, it seems, the modern way.

I tried to apologise but that was no good. I had done that too often before apparently, and he had god knows how many acres at home to cut and couldn't be waiting for me and so on. I am not the most sensitive person but I could see he was angry.

I could also see that I hadn't a leg to stand on. But even at that there comes a time when you feel you've taken enough abuse. Then I reminded him about the cart he couped two years ago, about the seven tramlines instead of two he had given me in last year's wheat and told him that the oilseeds he was tramping down had no tramlines for the second year running.

Well, of course, after that there was no way back. Harvest was finished for the year and I got a new contractor who came at once and sowed our sixty acres of wheat.

It was the end, at least for the moment, of a relationship which had worked with varying degrees of success, for over thirty years and, as such, it was sad. There were once thirteen years on the trot when he didn't send me a bill. As a friend said to me at the time, "You canna very well go past a lad like that."

But I've done it now.

Waster takes up challenge

THE BREADWINNER would have another holiday and I was again favoured to accompany her, for a week in Malta. After our harvest which spanned four months I felt she could afford it. So off we went.

Now, you have heard me refer to my younger son as the Wasting Asset after his lifestyle of summering in the Med. where he runs nightclubs. Well, now he has taken rent of one of our empty cottar houses and runs clubs in the toon as well as a monthly rave at the new mart at Thainstone.

He is usually far too busy when it comes to real work but he agreed to be grieve for a week and do my work for me.

I may have to stop being so hard on the lad for he took up the challenge and not only fed my beasts but wrote this diary as well. I found it on the kitchen table when I got back.

Thank God that's him off the place for a while. It'll give me a chance to get things tidied up. He may be a good farmer but he always leaves such a mess. And it's more than that. The way he leaves things just creates work.

Take the feeding of silage bales to the cattle. The Farmer will dump the bale, cut a hole in the wrapping and let the cows do the rest. That is OK at feeding time but what happens is that the plastic cover and the netting or string that keeps the bale together gets pulled into the pen among their feet. Then at muck-spreading time you have to stop after every second load to cut the strings off the hammers of the mucking cart. I am the one who tends to get the mucking to do so I've nagged him for years, but what can you do with a bloke who finally says to you, "I ken fine you're richt but I'm jist nae daein it."?

He has a habit of saying "If you want a job done right dae it yersel", so he knows what to do.

Anyway I enjoy looking after the beasts. I've always liked cattle and it is so good now that he has got rid of the

122

Jerseys. I called them 'Kamikaze cows' because there seemed to one legs-up every morning. Now that we have the black Herefords and pure Simmies I can look out each morning and be fairly sure they'll all have their legs pointing at the grass.

It wasn't all plain sailing though. He left me the job of worming the fourteen new hill cows he bought last week. They were fairly needing it and he assured me that they would be so busy eating their cobs each morning that I would be able to apply the stuff using this gun thing.

Unfortunately the cows didn't see it that way. The sight of the Wasting Asset advancing on them with this gun made them set off as though I was going to 'waste' them. They kept coming back to the cobs though and eventually I found that I could get within about six feet of them by charging from behind. Then I pulled the trigger and some went on their backs, some went on their sides and some was spread to the seven winds.

After ten minutes or so I was quite out of breath but happy that I had got some wormer on all the cows. I had nearly emptied the bottle of Ivomec by this time and I was slightly perturbed when Po-tions the chemist informed me that it cost a hundred pounds a bottle. Still, if he wants the job done right he can take his own advice.

Everything is very wet and the bank of the river is lined with fishermen in a way that it hasn't been for years of pollution and drier conditions. I could see six along the bank of the cows' four acre park. They will live a long time for they say that God doesn't count time spent fishing in the three score and ten he alots us.

The sight reminded me of the time when I was about ten and I came home from the river with seven beautiful finnock (as we call first run sea trout). I was intensely proud of my catch and gladly accepted the praise that was heaped on my head. For many years I kept the photo of myself with my seven beauties. I have just a faint prick of conscience now, that I forgot to tell everyone that a kindly middle-aged man had thrown six of my catch across the river to me as he simply didn't have any more room in his fridge.

I did think of holding a rave in one of the sheds when they were away but decided against it despite the fact that the one I held in the old tattie shed a couple of years ago

made a profit far in excess of the value of the shed.

All in all I think the Farmer will be pleased when he gets home. Nothing has died, not even a pig. None of his old sheds has been knocked down by his new digger or fallen down when hit by the breeze, and none of the cattle has been in the neighbouring gardens.

All in all it has been fine having the place to myself and looking after the livestock. But I am not a real farmer. He'll tell you there is no sight in the world like a heavy crop of wheat waving in the wind or a herd of cows and calves chewing the cudd in the gloaming.

But for me nothing can beat the sight of seven hundred people leaving the mart having paid me fifteen pounds a head for the privilege of dancing all night.

Reivers set for raid down south

CROOKIE IS still not back from that honeymoon and we are worried. We reckon he is in Africa because he told Big Hamish before the wedding that he had been jabbed for aathing. That rules out Stonehaven and Strathpeffer, the traditional honeymoon spots, for a start.

What on earth would he be needing with a whole fortnight away with ninety acres of tatties in the ground? It hardly bears thinking about. We scan the papers for news from the trouble-spots of the Dark Continent but there has been no news yet.

I hope they don't suffer the fate of the couple who went for a whole two weeks game-viewing in Kenya. Like everyone else, apart from David Attenburgh, they found that they had seen enough lions and elephants after four days so they decided to go off by themselves for a do-it-yourself walking safari. They each packed their own knapsack with pack lunch, viewing glasses and camera.

Once they were thoroughly lost they sat down to have their sandwiches and consider whether the exercise had been a good idea. Just then a very hungry lion appeared and charged at them. The gallant husband tore open his knapsack, threw out the goggles, the camera and the sandwiches and produced a pair of rather natty trainers.

"What on earth good will those do you," said his lovely bride. "You'll never outrun a lion even with your fancy shoes."

"It's not the lion I'm going to try to outrun. It's you."

Anyway, we had an anxious wait but he didn't turn up to the discussion group on Sunday. Poor Mossie didn't turn up either. He's still scouring from the wedding. At least that's my theory though his wife, loyal creature that she is, is going along with his story that it is salmonella poisoning and nothing to do with the wedding.

I hope it's not because

preparations are well advanced for the great reivers raid on South East England since the news that the failure rate among what used to be the fat cats of the swinging city means that Porches, Range Rovers and Mercs are going for a song in the bankruptcy sales.

Well, Mossie has set up a tour company to provide short package holidays including a chance to steal reposessed status symbols. About twenty of us who have had a good harvest (rather than going on honeymoon in the middle of it) are booked on the first tour. For only three hundred pounds we get a flight to London, a day at Smithfield Show, a day at the auction, two nights in a reputedly very lively place called soHo (sic), and then we drive our new status symbols home in convoy up the M1.

I'm looking forward to it. Not that life is dull in the meantime.

This week we had the launch of old Sir Maitland Mackie's autobiography. He's the one who was for many years chairman of the Aberdeen and District Milk Marketing Board and who was honoured by the Queen and his University for his services to Agriculture before it was clear that his son and namesake (the current Vice President of the Farmer's Union) was going to make all that fuss.

Thus it was that we all trooped back to King's College for lots of drink, not much food and only two remarkably short speeches, neither of them given by the vice president of the union. Sir Maitland has called his book 'A Lucky Chap' which, if you read the book, you will see is just how he feels about his life.

For Sir Maitland has the gift of optimism. When he woke up from the abdominal operation and was told that they had cut him up, had a look and decided that it wasn't necessary, he didn't rush off and sue. He thought how lucky he was to have avoided the need for the operation. And what was an abdominal scar to a man who, when he found that he had a bad congenital condition which causes your little fingers to curl up, cheerfully ordered them cut off?

Sir Maitland considered himself lucky to have had eighty years and to have seen such changes in farming and in the farming life. He was lucky that his father, the first Maitland Mackie, had been on hand to kill the rat that fell on his bed from the hole the rottens had eaten in his bedroom ceiling. To have had a wonderful teacher who cheerfully belted all the boys in the class because she knew some of them were taking it in turns to use their dinner money to buy a packet of Woodbines.

He was especially lucky when he was a small boy and he had been chosen by his big brother John to be test pilot in the parachute he had designed. The designer is now Lord John-Mackie the Labour peer and his plan was that they would throw young Maitland off this ninety foot memorial to one of the Lords of Aberdeen. He would then float gently to earth supported by the air trapped in one of his mother's tablecloths. It would be just like they had seen in photographs of the airborne troops in the first war.

Mike looked down from the top of the tower and panicked just in time. Furious at his brother's cowardliness John agreed to trying a stone first. It thumped to the ground, its progress quite unimpeded by the parachute. The big brother agreed that a further period of experimentation was needed before the first manned flight. Lucky again you see.

127

Danger round the corner

A FARMER like me needs a stroke of luck now and again and I appear to have got it.

You see it has been my intention, since I returned from Kenya, to have a herd of forty hill cows on my Less Favoured Area land. I was wary of just going out and buying them at the going rate of maybe eight hundred pounds a piece, though, and would try my wild scheme of getting Jersey cows for under three hundred and transplanting beef embryos into them.

That was a great success when it was a success but that wasn't often. Fertility was low and the rate of attrition was high so that I never quite got to forty. I bought thirty black Hereford heifer calves two Aprils ago and they are now due to calve in the spring. That looked like good business as they only cost £56 and their feed bills have got lost among the rest.

But then came the MacSharry proposals. There would be quotas on the beef herd and everyone seemed to agree that those would be based on the numbers of cows you had in 1991 or 1990. That would mean 34 or 32 for me. I don't suppose there is much hope of the herd making a profit anyway but without the subbies it was clearly going to be hopeless. I might have thirty in-calf heifers but I would have no quota for them.

And then I had my stroke of luck.

The powers that be decided to make the base year for cow quotas 1992.

I have to say it was a very strange thing to do as 1992 isn't finished yet. That made little difference to the efficient farmers like the Red Rooster. They had counted their cattle and sent away their forms ages ago. But I had been forgetting to do so and postponing till tomorrow, so I had not. All I had to do was to buy a hundred cows and I could get quota to match.

Well, I decided not to be greedy. I have just bought enough cows to put me up to the forty which will be an ideal herd to fit in with the cereal-growing on Little Ardo. And as my old cows become too old, or go wrong among their feet I will be able to bring my black Herefords into the herd as replacements. A minor dream will be fulfilled.

Meanwhile the excitement is rising about the trip to London to scoop up the cars which are being repossessed from the high rollers who are going broke in droves in the sleepless city. I think Mossie has organised the trip because he is so worried about having me for a friend in case anyone sees my old Vauxhall Cavalier parked at Moss-side. He wants me to buy a six-litre Jaguar. It's called an XJRS, is automatic and he says it will pass anything on the road except a petrol pump.

That would be too much for me. Too much of a jump all at once. At the moment the Breadwinner and I have three ten year old Vauxhall Cavaliers between us on the theory that there should always be two working. And that's one thing that is holding me back from going too far up market. She goes off to town every day to her fancy job. And can you see her marching past my fancy Jaguar to get into one of the battered Vauxhalls? So I'm not altogether sure that Mossie has the car for me.

Actually, I don't think the XJRS will be big enough for the Farmer and that's not because he grew three tonnes fourteen of wheat this year. After last Saturday I won't feel safe in anything less than a Chieftain tank.

You may remember that a year and a half ago I was involved in what might have been a fatal smash on the way to the Mart. This car came round a rather nasty corner sideways at me at what I guessed was seventy miles an hour. There was nowhere for me to get off the road and had I pulled to the left I would only have struck a wall and he'd have come in my driver's door. So I held her straight and hit his back wheel. That sent him spinning into the woods while I got a whiplash which still keeps me awake at night with a sore neck.

Well now, on Saturday I was again proceeding to the Mart. At that very same corner I met a fire engine doing maybe as little as sixty. He was hard onto the white line and only just, it seemed to me, holding the road. If he had lost it there would have been nowhere for me to go and I could not have sent him spinning into the woods.

I didn't stop but I was quite faint after that. I am going to need counselling.

The need for that became the greater when I discovered that the hurry that nearly cut my mortal coil was only to get to Mossie's drier. Farmers in the south will find it hard to believe that harvest is still proceeding between snow storms up here in Aberdeenshire, but such is the case. And Moss-side still hasn't finished drying his linseed. Well, he has now. For the drier finally gave up at the last load and went into spontaneous combustion.

Of course Mossie has never suffered from a lack of faith in his own ability and he has been telling us all year that he would have at least a tonne and a half of linseed to the acre, about three times the national average. We all knew that even he could not manage that. But now we're not so sure.

This year's yield will no longer be determined by the weigh-bridge but in negotiations with the insurance company.

Our man is a fair negotiator.

Lessons to be learned from the wedding

CROOKIE'S BACK from the honeymoon in Mauritius and he's pleased. Not only was the holiday all it was cracked up to be but his brothers had got all his tatties up during the two weeks that he was away.

That was more than anyone had expected. Little progress was being made when the groom left the most valuable crop on the place to the best man and the usher. It was a cool thing to do, but he got away with it. The monsoon petered out. The wind rose and the boys worked hard to save their brother's crop. They knew he would be needing all the money he could get to support his new lifestyle.

Now, you might think the brothers would be embarrassed by the praise that would be heaped on them for doing no less than saving the financial year. But you'd be wrong. All the groom said was, "Aye boys, I kent you'd have got them up. Ilka mornin I looked oot and saw the sun

was shinin. Oh, you were bound to get the tatties up in weather like that."

Mind you, all was not entirely well. A mousie had been to work in the honeymooner's houseful of presents. It had eaten a great big hole in the settee they got from the wife's mother. What a blow! Mossie says he can't understand why they don't make settees with warfarin linings - a simple precaution that could have saved so much embarrassment.

Isn't it just typical? They only got the one three-piece suite and the mousie had a go at that. Why hadn't it gone for the cafetieres? I don't know how many of those they ended up with, but when we went round with ours it was put in a place of honour as far as possible from the two they had been given already.

Mind you that wasn't as bad as my boyhood pal who is now the plumber in the village. When he got married they were pleased to receive

131

thirteen companion sets. And worse still, they were going to live in a caravan.

Anyway there have been a lot of lessons learned from Crookie's wedding. Not least that weddings should be held a bit earlier in the year. He's still too much in love to come to Smithfield with the boys.

I haven't told you how the pigs have been doing for some time. But they are doing and they are not losing money. You will recall that I bought four hundred weaners at the top of the last boom. They cost just over forty pounds to buy. They ate just over £27 worth of feed and sold for seventy-three pounds.

So I had a fiver to pay for my labour, for the amenity loss of having the smelly brutes about the place, all the disgusted looks when I went down to the shop for my paper, and to pay for the four that died.

In other words I would have been as well to stay with the deal I had with Grampian Country Pork which gave me four pounds a pig and no risk.

It was Mossie who persuaded me to go on my own. He seems to be able to get over ten pounds a pig every time.

He's away again. He filled up at 104 pence a kilo and he's sending them away fat this week at 115. He's just bound to have eleven pounds a pig without the blawin. And he's sneaky. He had his all safely bought before he told the discussion group that it was time to buy.

Well, I've mine bought too. I was really pleased that I got them tuppence cheaper than he did, but I might have known not to try to rub that in. "Aye, but you're six weeks behind. And have you seen the future's price if you miss Christmas?"

I have now. It's due to drop thirteen pence a kilo (about ten pounds a pig). Anyway they are home and doing fine except the three that died in the first ten days.

Mind you, this speculation in pigs may have to stop for want of straw. The stuff we used to burn on washing days and on Sundays when the townspeople were out for a drive, is as scarce as hen's teeth and in far greater demand.

Straw stored inside is now worth between eight and eleven pounds a bale. I reckon to bed them well.

The piggies need half a bale each, so that is another fiver on to the costs. If the job was marginal before it is certainly no good with the boys from the Northern Isles will-

132

ing to pay all that for straw.

I'd like to sell some, but I'll need more straw to get my cows through the winter, as with my increased numbers and my thirty in-calf heifers, I have twice as many adults as last year.

Mossie goes daft over Rodmobile

WHEN ANEURIN Bevan was a young Welsh miner in the 1930s, he and his pals went for their first excursion from the Valleys to London. Nye had a new coat, and it was on its first outing. Being used to a haircut costing thrippence, and being fully aware that in London it could be dearer, he went into a place in Oxford Street for a crop. They sent him out looking very tidy, but with no money and no coat.

Well, I have to report that The Farmer, who normally pays £2, three times a year, for a crop in the village, has been for a haircut in Harrods, no less. But he was luckier than poor Bevan. The discussion group subscribed £2 each towards the deal.

A very engaging young lady who wanted to talk about

the political situation in South Africa and had no idea what a wet year we'd had, washed the hair first. Then she cut it, blew it dry, spiked it up at the front, and sent him out to face the boys looking the way Bill Haley looked 30 years ago, but with the quiff standing up instead of curling down.

I was pleased enough. I gave the girl a tip of £2, which meant my haircut came in at the usual price. And the boys were quite right. I realised it when the grain of barley came out in the washing. The hairdo was necessary to complete the move up-market.

You see, we've been to London and we've all bought yuppie cars - even me.

As you know it was Mossie's idea. He'd heard that the City of London was having such a hard time that the fat cats and whizz kids were unloading Porsches and Mercs at rockbottom prices at a roup called Blackbushe. Fair enough, the lads would go and, as it was the same time as Smithfield, we'd get the trip through the books.

The Mart was a high-security-fenced sea of the most beautiful cars you could imagine. Mercs by the dozen, Rolls Royces, Bentleys, Jaguars. This was the top sale, and the boys from the North did look a bit out of their depth. Mind you, the Red Rooster had something called an ADT card, which meant we could buy as many as we wanted.

One of the star buys was a custom-built, three feet high, 200 miles an hour nightmare which was the property of a singer called Rod Stewart. No wonder he wanted rid of that. But Mossie was impressed. When he saw the Rodmobile he was over knocking at the windows and calling to Rod to appear. And other customers were amazed to see this middle-aged farmer down on his knees calling up the enormous exhaust pipes: "C'mon oot Rod. We ken ye're in there."

When the car was brought into the ring Mossie welcomed it with a burst of "Sailing," and I really feared he was going to make a purchase. He didn't. It was eventually bought by a pale, nervous-looking man at the back, who outbid an extremely heavy looking duo at the front. They exuded menace, wore pigtails and diamond knuckle-dusters, and chewed gum aggressively. That one made £61,000, and I was glad the auctioneer didn't have the doric when the next car, a modest BMW came in. "Stan' on," roared Mossie.

Ashley Thom, who is top hand at Maitland Mackie's outfit, broke our duck - buying a one year old Land Rover Discovery for little more than half price. They were still congratulating him when the most beautiful Jaguar seemed to stick at £8600. It was metallic blue, immaculate, registered in 1990 and had £6000 worth of extras, including a 32-piece orchestra which appears at the press of a button to give impromptu concerts.

The farmer was sure he wouldn't get it.

But one wink and he did. "Pen Two" roars Mossie, and that did it. If Charlie was going to be driving a thing like that, a general move up-market was definitely on. Soon we all had status symbols, and the transporter had to be ordered.

Out came the mobile phone (at a car auction everyone has a mobile phone). "Why the hell should you get a special price?"

"Because I am special," said our negotiator, a man called Nicoll from Keith.

So now I have a car that will pass anything on the road except a petrol pump. I had thought of driving her home, but the only way that could be was if I sat in her on the transporter. It would just be too expensive on her own steam. In fact, though I will allow myself little luxuries like driving her down for the papers, if I want to go anywhere further than Aberdeen I will have to put her back on the transporter.

Safari Park as diversification sends shivers down my spine

HAVING READ of the closure of the Windsor Safari Park, no doubt the Breadwinner was pulling my leg when she suggested that a safari park might be worth considering as a suitable diversification for my few paternal acres.

The very idea sent shivers down my spine for two reasons.

Firstly, as you know, I have 30 in-calf heifers which are still outside. They have a 16-acre field of grass, 13 acres of wheat stubble, and five acres of permanent pasture. They get 2lb of cobs a day, and some truly disgusting bales of last year's straw.

You would think that would be enough for them, and perhaps it is - but they don't stay in their fields. As I write, I am awaiting the angry phone call that will tell me that they have made their fourth escape. Six of them have been down to the village. And seven of them have found their way into the Wasting Asset's garden - twice.

The damnable thing is that I can't find the weak link in my fences. If they were better, it would almost certainly be easier - but the whole lot are rotten posts and rusted wires, teetering on top of rickles of stones that were once dry-stane dykes, but which are now just dry stanes.

Each time there has been a breakout I have mended what seemed to be the weakest link in this ropey chain, but I have to confess that I haven't found a bit where there seems to have been enough traffic.

At any rate, you can see how I would hate to keep have to keep lions and antelopes in, when I can't keep a few Hereford-cross-Friesians at home. I recall my Kenyan

THAT'LL KEEP 'EM OUT!

8 ft.

friend, Mzee Ole Sein, who can't keep the giraffes out of his farm with an eight-foot fence. The great deer just rear up on their back legs, plant their fores on the other side, and then gracefully lift their back legs over.

And my other shudder at the thought of a safari park at Little Ardo is caused by the fact that I have had one here before.

It was in the late 1960s that I looked seriously at becoming a cattleman. At that time I had two cousins who were making money hand-over-fist out of importing Charolais cattle from France and selling them to Ameri-cans. These cattle were worth about £3000 apiece, but ate little more than your average cross cow - which was only worth about £200. I figured that if I could get over the initial expense, I would be able to mount the gravy train.

I joined the Charolais Cattle Society and duly got a couple of heifers from France. They cost less than £2000 apiece, so I was clearly on my way.

Then it was brought to my attention that there was an importation of another foreign breed, Simmentals, this time from Germany. It took a while to get used to the sound of the name, but they were to be Seminals, Sentimentals or, as the Aberdeen and Northern Marts called them for the next ten years - Charolais.

Indeed, having been first in, the Charolais got the blame for the ills of the whole foreign invasion. I remember being told in grave terms by one of the best known cattlemen in Scotland that the Scottish Milk Marketing Board had come to the conclusion that the only Charolais that were any use were the Seminals and the Belgian Blues.

Anyway, the Seminals only cost £400 apiece, and their calves were worth a minimum of £2500. I was clearly on my way to my first million. The search was on for more and different breeds of these wonderful European cattle.

Then came Gelbvieh and Limousine and Blondie-Aquitaine:

Normandaise and Murray Greys and Anjou Mains., There were MRIs and WRIs and Markie power, Romin-in-the-gloamin, Rotguts and Pinzegaur.

Every penny and more was invested (if that's the word) in exotic cattle until, the international oil crisis in 1973 killed the market stone dead. I was left with some of the most expensive meat in the world.

It was then that we tried "Charlie's Safari Park". People would pay a fortune, so the argument went, to drive in the safety of their cars through field after field of strange nowt.

It was a good idea, and a brave try, but it was a nightmare. Why should they pay to see these cattle which were so enormous that they could be seen quite clearly from the road? That is, if the cattle weren't on the road. For, bad as my fences are now, they were far worse then and Chianina cows can jump a four-foot gate with ease, lifting their back feet like steeplechasers.

With interest rates now at all-time highs, and three sheds under construction, my father very wisely decided he could stand it no longer and wanted out. I could buy the place at a knock-down price which afforded him a capital gain of 2,000% on his investment - and, of course, I would just pay his capital gains tax.

Well, I could hardly turn down an offer like that, so I became laird of the place with an overdraft that peaked at £1,000 an acre.

Do you wonder at my shuddering at the thought of another safari park?

Easy winter plan for a working fool

IT'S NOT just the best laid schemes of mice and men that gang agley. Most of mine seem to as well. Take my plans for a quiet winter, for example.

Mossie calls me the 'workin' feel' because I still have cattle about the place. He cannot understand why I should keep them. They don't make any money, they visit my neighbours in the night, and they have to be fed at times of day when the Grain Baron is still in bed, or at least enjoying a slow recovery.

So be it. My father once decided that he would retire from livestock and sold his dairy cows and all the followers. He got a quiet life alright, as he waited for the harvest each year. But the place was dead, an agricultural Marie Celeste. Two cats and the occasional rat aren't enough. I'm not going back to that no matter how much money the cattle lose.

But I did plan to make the winter as easy as possible. I would just have three lots to feed each day.

The cows would go in and out all winter, and they would be fed straw with a suppy syrup poured over it. I would fill up the centre pass of my slatted court with straw, and that would do the old girls for ever so long. Every week I would go in with the digger and push the remains to the end, and fill her up again.

Then I would have my 20-odd bull calves in the old dairy byre. They would get big bale silage at a feed barrier at one end, and a few pounds of concentrates in their feed trough which runs along one side. The heifer calves would get the same diet in the old barn, and go out to the midden to get their cake. Half an hour a day should easily feed the cattle, and you could hardly call the man with as little to do as that a "workin' feel."

But it isn't working out like that.

First of all there was the scheme to keep all the breeding cows together. That foundered because the traffic made their route to the park virtually impassable. As they spent all day every day going out to see if by any chance a blade of grass had been overlooked on the braes, and then back in again to see if I seriously expected them to survive on straw, they produced a deep, muddy swamp. So I separated the 30 in-calf heifers.

They would get straw in feed rings, and that means running down to their field with the digger twice every day.

Then my life was complicated by the fact that I didn't manage to get all my last year's stots off the grass. They would have to come inside for a few weeks to finish them on intensive bull nuts. Now, I really don't have a good system for dealing with those. They come in bulk, three tonnes at a time, and are blown into the grain cart. So every morning I have to bag some off for the feeding cattle and lug it round to them.

And, worse than that, I've got a few females I am feeding up as well. There are some that missed the summer market, and a couple of cows. One lost her calf, and the other forgot to have one.

And again, the quiet life depends on my cows all calving together in March and April. But already I have three calves and, of course, their mothers can't run with the rest. They need a better diet for a start, and the calves would be like to drown in the mud.

Then there is the old cow which we discovered in the early stages of staggers when we were doing our herd test. She needs a pen to herself, too.

And this morning I have discovered a whole new category. The cow that missed her last year's calf is now very fat and ready for the market - except that she is now making an udder. I'll need to get her onto starvation rations to see if there is still time to get some weight off before she calves. I need another individual pen.

So with nine lots of cattle to feed each morning, as well as the pigs to look at, I am indeed the working fool.

And I can't even say that the Jaguar is being much of a consolation.

I used to say that I didn't care a damn for my image. Proof of that was the fact that I always drove cars that had no scope for depreciation. My fleet of three diesel Cavaliers, with their total age of 30 years and up to 10% rust, could all be had for little over

£1000 - and I really didn't care if I looked a bit shabby.

But I was wrong. I do care about my image. I like it depressed. The two year old, three-litre Jaguar is all wrong for me. I don't like oozing prosperity, however spurious that may be. No one recognises me as I float along in my

my unsuitability for the move up-market, that I have entered her for the sale at Thainstone later today.

Of course I'll be looking for a bit of profit - and that may well not be easy, considering the expense of going to London to buy her.

I don't know what I'll do

status symbol. One of the joys of driving in your own country is waving to everyone you meet. But when I wave from my Jaguar I never get a wave back. I may as well be a stranger in a strange land.

So discouraged am I by

with the money, if I get it. I'm torn between say, 10 more Cavaliers and another 20 cattle to look after. I am, after all, more at home as a 'workin feel' than as a toff in what the Americans call a 'gas guzzler'.

Mossie the philosopher gets right up my nose

It's frost this week. There is always a something that comes and spoils what could be a tolerable existence on the margin between enough and plenty.

I told you last week how my plans for a quiet life with only three lots of cattle had been expanded to nine. Well, now I can tell you that three of those lots have had frozen pipes for too long, and not even my cattle can thrive without water.

It can be dangerous to let them go short of water too. A fringe member of the discussion group that meets to criticise our neighbours in the Salmon Inn on Sundays knows all about that. His stots had been frozen for a few days, and he was very fed up with the bucket. So, what he did was to fill up the muckspreader and give them two thousand gallons into their trough.

It was a kindness which went dramatically wrong. They drank it too quickly, and over 30 big stots died.

In the cold winter days cattle don't need much water, unless they are milking cows. We used to feed stots all winter without a drink and they never needed one so long as they were being fed on turnips. Everybody knows that the neep is 95 percent water, and we used to reckon that the thirst made them eat up - and helped them to hurry off to market.

But we don't grow any turnips now. In fact, we are trying to get the breeding stock through to the calving on straw and treacle which is a pretty dry diet, so the buckets have been out.

Not for them all, I hasten to add. The in-calf heifers are still outside, but there is no grass in their fields and only ice in their troughs. However

I have located a spring which is still running, and I have been able to get them water by taking down the intervening fence.

I did well with the cows and calves and the breeding heifers. I found that by cramming them in together I could so raise the temperature in their byre that the pipes stayed unfrozen.

But that still leaves the stots needing watered by bucket.

It reminds me of the old days when hereabouts all cattle were tied in stalls all winter and had to be bucket-fed water twice a day. It took hours if it was done honestly, which was not always the case. There is a story of a young single man who grumbled about having to bucket water 40 steers when he was on duty every second weekend. No one took any notice until the grumbling stopped. Then they were highly suspicious, and the grieve made enquiries, whereupon the loon revealed that it was much easier if you put just a wee touch of sharn in the pail. That way, a few bucketsful did the trick.

Now that was all very well for the loon. He was cheating the master. But I am the master, so I have no alternative to bucketing away.

And have you any idea how much a cow with a calf will drink?

I was toiling away at it on Sunday afternoon when my guide, neighbour, and mentor, the farmer of Moss-side, turned up. Now, I can take Mossie as all of these things, but when he becomes the philosopher he gets right up my nose. With no word of giving a hand, but with much sighing and the occasional spit, he opined: "Aye Charlie, it's times like this that you wish you had stuck in at school."

As well as being damnably annoying, he's wrong. I did stick in at school and covered myself with glory, though damn the bit of good did it do me. Where do they teach you at school about watering steers? Where does it tell you to do whatever it is the Canadians do to get their cows through winters at 40 degrees of frost? Where does the school tell you to sell the cows and let others be the 'working fools'? The answer is - nowhere. And Mossie, who saw the school primarily as a place for trying out an emerging talent for wit, humour, and getting on people's nerves, he's got all that useful information.

The news and the outlook are not all bad however.

I took the Jag to the car

144

It's times like this you wish you had stuck in at school!

auction at Thainstone with a heavy heart. I had washed her, the first time I had washed a car since 1965. I had felt her smooth dentless flanks, admired my reflection in her gorgeous chip-free bonnet, and polished up at her stainless steel till she shone like the cars my friends drive.

As we ghosted through the countryside at eighteen point three miles to the gallon, I despaired of myself for bottling-out of the move up-market for which the boys had worked so hard in London. It was they who got me to buy her - and to have my hair cut in Harrods.

I had a few cards up my sleeve though. I had forgotten to bring the bits of paper that would have allowed the auctioneer to say, "Service details since new." I nicked the license which still had eight months to run, and I then proceeded to act as shifty as possible when any prospective buyers came to look at her. Even so, she reached £8800. "Only a small bit short sir. I'm sorry." The auctioneer might have been sorry, but I wasn't.

As I ghosted my car home to her garage in the old tattie-shed, I reflected that things could have been a lot worse.

And the nichts are fairly beginning tae draw oot.

Hillie gets revenge by topping up my glass

WE HAD the whole family for Christmas dinner. That meant the two Investments, the Wasting Asset and the Recovery Stock, three adorable little Investments for the next generation, one wife, one husband, and a brace of the 'ither grandparents'.

Fourteen for lunch, if you count the turkey, made a very jolly occasion.

During the meal I found myself reflecting on the changes in the relative importance of Christmas and the New Year on the farms of Buchan.

I told them that until some time in the 1950s Christmas wasn't even a holiday. My father had a turkey, not really to celebrate the nativity, but because he liked a turkey and they were only available at Christmas in those days. But his five men worked on as if nothing had happened 2000 years earlier.

We had neighbours then who had retired from a fancy job in the BBC in Edinburgh and, that not being an ideal background for farming, our men got the job of growing their crops for them. As a thankyou to the men, a bottle of whisky appeared at dinner time on Christmas day.

James Low, the grieve, knew fine what to do with whisky. He made the three outside lads produce the lids off their flasks, split the bottle in four, saw that they drank it down in a one-er, and sent them home to their dinner.

They were all back at one o' clock as though it had been any other day. That was the only sign of Christmas I can remember among the men on the farm when I was young.

But the New Year was altogether different.

Hogmanay itself was a working day, though the pub and the general merchants in the village were always active in the morning. That was when many of the backwoodsmen would come out to pay their account, rather than start a new year in debt.

The merchant would give a dram as a luckpenny - and even a bottle if it had been a big account, or one that he had despaired of getting.

But that sort of business was for the masters. The men worked on until half past five as usual. Only the dairy cattleman had to work the next day, and that is maybe just as well - for, building on a slow start, the great pagan festival had taken a severe toll by morning.

But sore heads or not, it was on New Year's day that the bairns got their presents, and that the great meal was enjoyed. Aye, changed days.

There is a glazed look that comes over the eyes of my offspring when I tell them of the old days, and so it was when I was telling them about Little Ardo in Christmases past.

The Wasting Asset had been listening though. "Aye," he said. "It's fairly different noo. Instead of six men working on Christmas day, you've got it a tae dae yersel."

"That is true, but officially it is a holiday. If I had still had six men they would have had a holiday this Christmas, whereas on New Year's day they would always have had a holiday." I tell you it is not easy to educate the young, even when they're not as young as they were.

I missed Santa again this

147

year. My children have long been amazed at the fact that the old saint of giving always makes his appearance when I am down at the Salmon having a quick half with the boys before the turkey.

And this year the astonishment entered a new generation - as the granddaughters were so disappointed for me that, just when I was called away to get some cattle which had escaped into the gardens of the village, the big man in red should come to dispense the expense from under the tree.

Each year the giving becomes more obscene - for everyone else. They got video games, CD players, mobile communications centres, and all of modern life to which I cannot relate. I got sensible presents. Long John thermals, from the Breadwinner who knows that if she loses me there will be no one daft enough to rise and feed these cows all winter, socks from the young Investment, a T-shirt from the Recovery Stock and sweatshirt from the Wasting Asset, and half an electric toaster from the older Investment.

I bought the Breadwinner secateurs, but spoiled the effect by leaving them in the glove box of a car which I had lent to the younger Invest-ment's young man.

It may be a sign of the times, but there have been many more practical presents among the peasants of Aberdeenshire this year. Prize among them all goes to Gowanwell. He gave his wife a spanking new Frazer muckspreader. I may say that she was absolutely delighted until she discovered that one of her sons had had a shot of it on the twenty-third, and that her handsome gift was now covered in sh... you know what.

If Christmas day had ended with the turkey and the presents I would remember it with more affection. But we stupidly went to a party. Hillie was there, and I let it slip that the Christmas tree I had taken from his plantation was even better than last year's. I was astonished that he regarded that as theft, despite my explaining that I hadn't stolen it. I had taken it - as usual. Wasn't that where everyone got their Christmas trees?

Anyway, Hillie got his revenge. He was most attentive and hardly left my side all night. He kept topping up my glass, and I kept on emptying it. By twelve o' clock I'd have given him his tree back had I but known where it was.

First footing in the auld style

WHEN I was a lad, first footing hereabouts used to mean stotting from house to house with a bottle of whisky and a bottle of sherry. The hostess at each house used to produce glasses about the size of thimbles and you poured everyone in the room a thimble of whisky for the men and a thimble of sherry for the women.

You then received a thimbleful out of the bottles belonging to everyone in the room and within half an hour you'd be off to the next venue.

That was a good system. The walking from house to house through the winter air and the minute size of the glasses meant you could get round a lot of folk and still feel human in the morning. It was always much more jolly than the Hogmanays we enjoy now.

It is partly because of the horrendous consequences of breathing too much when you are driving that has stopped the house-to-house first footing. Now you get invited to a party which is very static. There are few people to be wished a happy New Year, so there is more time for drinking. But the real deterioration in Hogmanay has been caused by the enormous growth in the size of the whisky glass. Gone are the nip glasses which were good enough for our fathers, and in have come great troughs like the ones our great grandfathers drank toddy from.

The result is that, when you go to the Hogmanay party nowadays, you are handed a glassful of whisky that would choke a horse. You then fill up the rest of the glass with water thinking that will make it less lethal and, of course, it makes it worse because half-and-half whisky goes straight into the bloodstream and from there to the head.

The whole thing is made worse by the old men who remember how everyone used to have a drink with everyone else and so insist on replenishing the trough every time you have a sip of it. The result is alcoholic poisoning on a scale unknown forty years ago.

You may have guessed that what I have just analysed is my Hogmanay of 1992. If you have you are close because that is how things went for me in 1991. This year I resolved to drink in the old manner and to see to it that my guests did likewise.

The old nip glasses were looked out and when Mossie and the Wasting Asset came in with some of their few remaining friends they were astonished to be offered a Lilliputian nip, to see their host, so well known for his excess, propose the New Year and dash it down, then, worst of all, not to fill it up again. It's not often that you see Mossie at a loss for words.

As they have lost the habit of carrying their bottles that soon got rid of them. I could hardly take the nip glasses with me but when we, in turn, set out to do our first footing, I insisted on getting no more than a tot and in drinking it neat in the old manner. We got round far more people and I managed a four-day Hogmanay without a hangover and without knocking down any of the walls in the steading when feeding the beasts each morning.

Not only that but I managed to get caught up with some of my paper work. I managed to reply to a number of the letters that have been hanging about on my desk and, only sixteen days late, I managed to fill in my Agricultural Return.

It is well known that, of all the jobs there are on the farm, filling up Government forms is the one I hate most. I had meant to appear brave at the prospect of turning my attention to the Return when the Breadwinner, who has a healthy scepticism of all my efforts as a farmer said, very unkindly I thought, "I don't know what all the fuss is about. I know the rape form is difficult and the suckler cow form and the variable premium. But the Agricultural Return form is easy. There you just have to put down the truth."

I got it done despite the fact that the truth is not always obvious there.

And I got the last of my Simmental-cross-Jersey stots off to the market. They graded O, 4, L or H and averaged £517 a head (with the sub to come). At nineteen months old that seemed to me to be pretty good as their mothers cost me almost nothing and had been kept comfortably by the Hill Livestock and Suckler Cow money. Of course it was the ones which

150

didn't calve which let the equation down.

The Breadwinner and I have now survived one another through thirty-three winters and I have to tell you that it is despite a pretty heavy incompatibility. I hate central heating and she hates the cold.

As the Breadwinner, she naturally calls the tune on that and when she is at home she makes sure that at least the taps in the bathroom don't freeze. In fact it is too hot for me in the upstairs of our house all winter because as hot water rises the pipes are are always hot even with the central heating pump off.

But when she goes off to work I can have the house as cold as I like. And I do.

I had Mossie in for his coffee the other day. I had been working and was lashing sweat. As a gentleman farmer he was thin of the blood that morning and only recovering slowly. When I handed him his coffee he shuddered, looked longingly at the sun shining through the frosted windows and said, "Could we nae hae wir coffee ootside?"

Renewable fuel source for Jaguar

I AM wrestling with my conscience and with Mossie.

You see the local co-op has got a contract to grow oilseed rape for non-food purposes on that set-aside land. That looks too good to be true, doesn't it? Oh, the papers will have a field day. "Farmers paid not to grow rape, to be paid to grow rape!"

When I got the letter offering me the chance to grow a decent crop which could provide a renewable source of fuel for the Jaguar, I was very pleased. As I have told you many times, I am an ancestor worshipper like most peasants and as such, I fear the wrath of my great progenitors if I set their acres aside.

My great-great-grandfather didn't drain the moss so that I could grow nothing on it and collect EC grants. My grandfather didn't build the barn with its fine empty loft, for it to stand empty. And yet, as a cereal grower, it looked as though I would have no alternative but to set one acre in seven aside.

So I would jump at the chance to grow a real crop on my set-aside and appease the ghosts of Farmers Past - and get £25 an acre extra margin into the bargain.

I phoned the great Grain Baron in some excitement in an effort to be the first to tell him the news. I was hurt and astonished by his reaction to my naive enthusiasm. "Oh aye," he sneered, "you're the Workin Feel, aye lookin for mair tae dae."

"But Mossie, look, I'm to get an extra £25 an acre for my 27 acres of set-aside. That's nearly £700. And that's 35 bottles of malt whisky." I could see him hesitate at that. He was calculating how many bottles of good malt he would earn if he turned his 150 acres of set-aside into industrial rape.

But no. He regards set-aside as the ideal break crop. Treated with the Moss-side Secret Formula, the set-aside ground will yield such a crop of wheat in 1994 as to dwarf £25 an acre. It is clear that the only way I can grow rape on my set-aside is to break with my Honorary Crops Adviser, and I just don't know how you would do that.

It is a battle between Mossie and my conscience, and I'm afraid that is a very unequal struggle. So 27 acres of the land of my fathers must lie fallow in 1993 and I'm not happy about it.

If I am sulking a bit with my agronomist, I am well pleased with my new con-tractor. He has taught me a lot in our brief association. He has taught me that action is possible in a calm. I had believed that if you were getting on with the work on the farm there had to be a lot of shouting, running back and forth, throwing tools, and bad language.

When Davie is on the case you might think that nothing was happening at all. And yet, suddenly, the work is done. It takes a bit of getting used to.

So do all those neat tramlines he's left in all the fields he's sown. Every field the same, and fitting my sprayer. It compares favourably with last year when we had two fields of barley that were up to 10% extra tramlines.

In 30 acres of wheat we had three acres of extra tramlines (and yet it still yielded three tonnes twelve). We were a bit latchie at harvest time last year, and this week we still had 40 acres of much needed straw lying. That doesn't worry me as wheat straw keeps well and dries completely when the winter winds turn dry, but it is always a relief to get it.

It was the ill wind that so devastated the mainland of Shetland that blew me some good, and I was phoning Davie at first light. The straw was dry - had he the baler greased?

"Aye," said the man of few words.

"That gale has dried the wheat straw up perfect. If you could come and bale it we could ... "

When I had finished a lot more excited chatter the quiet man said nothing.

"Davie? Are ye still there?" I asked excitedly.

"I'm thinkin."

After he had thought it all out, and within half an hour, he had arrived, not with one but with three balers. "Jist in case o' rain."

Then it was ACTION. It was a brave scene for January; three big John Deeres with dust flying out the back of them, and each stopping every few minutes to lay a great round egg. I had 40 acres of beautiful straw by dinner time - when the rain came on.

I also got Davie to spray the rape because the 590, which is my only tractor fit to pull the sprayer, was in dry dock. He would use my sprayer so he just charged me for two hours of himself and tractor.

Now that is all very well but that is my job. And I can't compete. Am I to be redundant altogether? His hourly bill comes to 66p an acre, against the spraying company's £3 or thereby. I don't suppose he'd take the whole contract at that rate, but I'm going to hurry to pay that account before he changes his mind.

Mucking into sea of slurry

AFTER ALL the times I have referred to his not knowing how much a percent was, I suppose I shouldn't be surprised at Big Hamish taking the chance to take me down a peg - but I did think it was a bit unnecessary. Everybody else seems to think it was very funny, so I suppose it must have been.

You see, the slats in the shed in and out of which I am wintering the cows, had become quite full. Only one of the three suction points was yielding any slurry and it was only clearing six square yards of slats, and that only lasted for a week at a time.

I was living in fear of The Cruelty if I forgot them for more than a week. So we got the big man to come with his new digger, the one that cost as much as his house, to muck out the slurry tanks. That was to be no easy job and involved lifting the 120 slats and scooping the priceless fertiliser into a cart with the back acter.

You may find this hard to believe, but such is the enthusiasm of Potions that he made up the squad. Potions and I were to lift five slats, Hamish would muck that into the cart, and then Hamish and I would replace the slats while Potions emptied the cart. Work study perfect.

But we found that the lifting of the slats which had been in place for some 15 years was difficult. No doubt the fact that they had been immersed in strang for so long had made the slats swell, or whatever the cement equivalent of rusting is - but it was a very stiff job indeed.

That was until I had the idea of using my digger to lift them. I would put the old 50B on the slats, slide the graip down between them, and tilt the bucket. Given that the slats were nine inches broad, and the lines of the bucket were three feet eight inches long, that would give me five slats. I would then reverse, Hamish would muck them out, I would drive forward again and it would be a dawdle to replace the slats and lift some more.

The theory was right again. It was the practice that was disappointing.

I don't know exactly what happened, though I do know the exact outcome.

Roughly, I got the five slats to lift alright, but four, it seems, would have been better. The fifth one started to fall off. I tried to catch it by tilting the graip and moving forward. That looked like a success, except that I was rapidly approaching the hole.

I then rammed on the clutch in a panic to stop myself but, as you will appreciate with the sort of modern machinery that I now have, the clutch was in fact the torque pedal. Thank goodness it wasn't forward I hit or I'd have been down the hole, but reverse was bad enough. I shot into reverse, which sent the first four slats plopping into the sea of thick slurry.

As we had just started, the digger didn't have far to go before it ran smack into the wall at the end of the shed. I was so relieved when I looked round to see that I had done no damage at the back, that I forgot to take my hand off the lift for the graip - which rose and rose until it pierced the big sixes on the roof.

I remember thinking: "Thank heavens everything

156

has reached its limit, all the slats are down the hole, the digger is hard against the wall, and the graip is fully extended and can't demolish any more of the roof.

Now, considering that everybody knows that Hamish is one of the best digger drivers there is, considering that he wins prizes for ten pin bowling with the digger, and considering I had been so generous in my praise for the speed and accuracy with which he was aiming the five slat hole and filling the cart, I thought he might have let that pass, but no.

"Aye, Charlie," he said, "I maybe canna write, but you fairly canna drive a digger."

That was greatly to the amusement of Big Hamish and Potions, which would have been bad enough, but it was also enjoyed by the Wasting Asset and Mossie, who can always smell trouble. I was clearly outvoted, so I had to laugh too.

From then on, I let Hamish drive both diggers, which worked well.

Anyway, we got the job done in two half days, and that was a great relief. Now I will be able to go for my last look round the cattle, surely the stock farmer's finest consolation, without fearing accusing looks from my beauties as the gleaming sludge threatens the side of the slats.

More than that, and this would astonish non-farmers, there is beauty in 120 slats when they are passing clean and keeping your stock dry.

It wasn't just the digger that was at work on the steading roofs this week. The wind made off with another few sheets of the asbestos my grandfather put up in the thirties. That sent me scuttling to the insurance policies.

157

White Hunter puts phone out of action

I NEARLY didn't go down to the Salmon for the discussion group on Sunday. The snow had come on again, and it was blowing. I couldn't see many of the boys making it in weather like that. The chances of being snowed-in certainly looked high. But then, I suppose there are worse places to be snowed into, and worse ways to spend the winter than marooned in a pub with your pals.

To my delight, everyone else had taken the same view and we had a full house. As the storm raged round the old Inn we drew close to the good log fire and shook our heads at the prospects of making it home on such a night.

It was the first time Crookie had made it this year, as he's been so busy with the new wife. He had two acres of potatoes left in the ground last backend. When I opined that he surely could have got the two acres up and finished the job, he shook his head. "I had plenty of rotten tatties in the shed already."

He tells me that it costs £1400 an acre to grow potatoes these days, and that he needs 19 tonnes to the acre to break even. And to think I used to grow about 10 tonnes. What a good day it was when I sold my quota to the Red Rooster.

No doubt he can grow 20 tonnes and may have justified his purchase, but the quota is now worthless and I cannot understand the bravery of those dairymen who are hanging on to their quotas. They are worth a fortune, and yet they will disappear one day leaving an awful lot of light balance sheets.

Mossie told us all about how busy he had been. Oh yes? What does a Grain Barron find to be busy at when the ground is in the grip of winter? "I've been planning," he says, "fit wey tae mak the best o' MacSharry, and fit tae dae wi aa the money I'm gan tae mak."

Big Hamish had heard on the wireless that time spent in your bed didn't count towards your three score years and ten, and he told Mossie that he would likely live for ever for all the hard work he ever did.

There was just a hint that things could get unpleasant so, after putting another log on the fire, I started in to tell them about the red face I got over the telephone being off.

Last Sunday night I took it off the hook because I wanted to go to bed at ten, and there was no sign that it would stop ringing of its own accord. On Monday morning when I put her back on, she was as dead as a doornail. That gave me four frustrating days.

Half the local engineers had been pulled away south to help with the trouble on Tayside, so when we got our share of the wind there was only a skeleton repair staff. I was quite cross by the time the engineer came on Thursday. He took a long time to find the fault, but eventually appeared with a steely look in his eye. "Have you been having a shoot, SIR?"

My heart sank. I had indeed had a wee shoot on Saturday. There was the joiner, the White Hunter, Potions and a pal of his who has a gun dog. I knew immediately what had happened. We were on our last drive and a pheasant got up from between the White Hunter's legs. It flew directly away from him and was surely the easiest possible target. And yet the White Hunter - the best shot there, and the man who claims to have shot a hundred cushet doos with ninety-nine shots - missed.

There had been quite a bit of leg-pulling about that, but not half as much as there would have been if we'd known that he had filled the telephone wires with pellets. He had weakened the wire, which had broken in the first real wind.

I shudder to think what the bill will be.

There was another unexpected drama on the shoot. We were the subject of a demonstration in favour of animal rights. We were shooting the little woods round one of the cottar houses which we let out, when the tenant opined that we must have awful little to do. And shortly the lady of the house was telling us that we should be ashamed of ourselves, and asking how we would like it if someone was to come after us with a gun.

I was rather impressed. It takes a lot of guts to tell people that you disapprove of what they are doing, especially if what they are doing is perfectly legal and commonplace, and if one getting the

earful is your landlord.

In fact (it was Potions who pointed it out) we would have been in no great danger unless the person after us with a gun had been a better shot than me. I had 10 shots that day and didn't hit a thing. Potions himself was little better. All he shot was a feral pigeon - and it was sitting on the barn roof.

Mossie put another log on the fire. "Aye Charlie," he said "you're going through a bad patch." Then he told Hillie to go and check the night to see if the road was blocked yet.

He came back sadly to announce that the wind had dropped, the snow had stopped, and that the road was still open.

There was no option but to go home though we had a clochandichter first.

Mystery of Mossie and the pigs

AWA' YE GO, AND MAK SICCAR THAT CHARLIE SEES YE!

BARGAINS PIG SALE BARGAINS

MOSSIE OFFERED me some pigs the other day. That put me on my guard of course. He doesn't usually have pigs to sell. In fact, in the normal run of things he can't possibly have any to sell because he has his pig unit finely tuned so that the throughput from service to slaughterhouse keeps his pigman fully employed, all day, every day. Every week the same number of sows are put to the boar, every week the same number go to the farrowing house, the same number are weaned and the same number of floats come trundling down the new dual carriageway to Mossside and park beside the plinth for the statue he's erecting to MacSharry.

So where was he going to get a couple of hundred weaners for his pal Charlie? I smelled a rat at once. "Well I'm going high health so I've to clear the auld lot oot," says he. "And what do you think

161

I'd be doing with low health pigs?" says I.

He explained, not that I understood, that high health pigs aren't high health at all. The point is that they aren't allowed near any germs. Now, most mammals get most of their germs from the herd and, in particular, from their mothers. The secret of the high health pig is that it doesn't have any contact with its mother.

The maternal chain by which mother passes all her diseases to her piglets is broken once and for all by hysterectomy birth and artificial rearing. Now, having gone to all that bother, you don't want to mix your high health piggies with your old low health ones so, to go high health, you have to clear the farm first.

Now do you see why he had some weaners to sell?

It looks like a lot of bother to me, but Mossie says the new pigs will never be ill (not that his old ones ever were either) and they'll convert better.

Maybe they will but, with all this MacSharry money that's coming in, and the extra they're now proposing on the acreage payments, and the money he's going to make from the early entry from set-aside to wheat, I don't see why he's bothering.

Unless it's boredom. There is so little to do these days. There is just the cattle to feed, and that takes a couple of hours a day even if you do a tidy job. The pigs feed themselves, and that leaves the crops. With all the frost we've had, it will be another fortnight before the ground has warmed up enough for any manure to be needed or any disease to think about growing.

We haven't even got the pigeons to shoot off the rape. With all the set-aside there is for them to scratch about in, and all the stubble which is bound for spring rape, they're just not interested in eating the rape leaves.

It was ever thus at this time of year. Even when I was a boy, and everything about the farm had to be done in the most difficult way possible, there were times when the grieve had a hard task to get enough for his five men to do in their 44-hour week. It was alright when the weather was open. Then there was the ploughing which, with double furrow, non-reversible ploughs, took a long time, and there was the constant slog to have enough neeps in, in case it would become hard. There were the periodic thrashes and the

162

tatties to dress, and of course the beasts were so difficult to sort then. But when the weather was coarse and we couldn't get on the land there was a lot of make-work. There was redding-up, sorting tattie sculls (baskets), and there seemed to be endless ropes and string to be sorted out and rolled into balls to accumulate in the loft.

But what I remember best about those stormy winter days, was a fire burning bursen oil in a home-made brazier in the tractor shed, and six men telling stories. That was magic to a boy and it fairly shortened the winter.

They told the old stories of the great men who were farmers, and who were men on the farms when Aberdeenshire was being tamed.

Like Geordie Gill who loaded 98 carts of muck in a ten-hour day, like Roch Annand, a man so strong that he could fill muck with a graip in each hand, and like Sandy Moir, who sharpened his scythe and left his stone at the gate. He had no need to carry it as he was so strong that he wouldn't need to sharpen it again until he had cut right round the field.

Those men had strength of body. But they had strength of mind too. Like James Low, who was sent by his employer, singlehanded, to gather the stones on a 40-acre field. As he went off with his graip, the farmer said: "Now, Low, dinna forget that a job well planned is a job half done."

Jimmy went up to the great park and sat down behind the dyke until dinnertime. When the farmer asked how the job was going, the man said - without a trace of a smile - that the job was half done already.

There's no-one on the farm nowadays for crack like that. There is only me now plus the amateurs, like Potions and the Wasting Assets from time to time. Aye, it can be lonely at times like this when there's nothing to do.

I'm sure that was what had got to Mossie with all this high health pig nonsense. He was just needing something to be doing.

163

Week is a long time in farming

Last week I said it would be another fortnight before the ground heated up enough to make it worth putting on the nitrogen. But it appears that a week is a long time in farming, for the first whiff of nitrogen is on the crop - and even on the grass.

The grass was growing even before the jumping nuts went on. It wasn't growing any taller, the beasts saw to that, but there were two bits of evidence. First the fields turned green, and second the cattle started to eat less straw. At the height of the frost the calving heifers were making off with two bales of straw a day. But that has shrunk to one, and then to only the tastiest half of one bale a day. The grass isn't getting a chance to grow any ranker, but it is growing.

There has been a dramatic spell of warmth, and what a good thing it is. About this time of year the Breadwinner usually insists on a week in the sun. That costs an arm and a leg to get down to Majorca or some other grotty venue.

And there we were last week with temperatures in Aberdeenshire higher than on the Western Mediterranean. We got the shirts off - and all at no cost.

I tell you it's exciting. Especially with the crops getting off to such an early spring. The oil-seed rape is looking well. It got its nitrogen on the Saturday when we had 16 degrees centigrade. We're usually lucky to get as many degrees fahrenheit. You could just about hear the stuff growing.

Davie, the contractor, usually puts his bonnet down when he finishes a load of manure so that he knows where to start with the next load. But the effect of the jumping nuts was so immediate on Saturday that he was able to keep the bonnet on all day. By the time he came back with another load, the manured rape was a clear half-inch higher and three shades greener - so he could see clearly where to start.

Yes, things are getting better at an alarming rate. The

acreage payments for rape are now over £200 an acre, and the price has taken off. The planners didn't seem to notice that if they got us to grow less of it the price might rise. And the wheat? Mossie, who always seems to get a bit more of everything than the rest of us, has been bid £120 a tonne at harvest ex-farm - and he'll get the MacSharry money as well.

I tell you it is exciting.

And the price of the manure's down as well. We all applauded the collapse of communism, but I don't think we realised what a boost it would be to the grain barons of North-East Scotland. I remember 19 years ago getting a load of nitrogen off a boat at a cost of £50 a tonne. Since then, with inflation, I have been none surprised to pay as much as £120. And yet the jumping nuts we put on this spring (it is urea) is only £60 a tonne on an equivalent basis.

I suppose that's 'deflation'.

And we're getting another boost. MacSharry is paying us to set land aside and to sow spring rape so that we'll have smaller crops. And he's reimbursing us for the money he thinks we'll lose as a consequence. I've aways remarked on the joys of shortages pushing up the prices, but there's another boon that good old Ray forgot. The unploughed stubble waiting for the spring rape and the set-aside, means the pigeons have more food than they know what to do with, so they're not bothering with the rape.

In recent winters my main job has been to run around with Willie the Hunter firing off my 12-bore to keep the blue horde off the rape. Now Big Mac is doing that for me. Mossie can hardly stop giggling about it. "Here's MacSharry paying us to grow less, but with the doos keeping off the rape we'll grow more." It's exciting all right.

Mind you there are snags. I have two fields of wheat which are very thin. It was very slow to germinate (about six weeks) and it looks healthy, but very late and very thin. There doesn't seem to be more than about a 100 plants per square metre, but there are no bare bits, so it looks like poor germination rather than beasties or disease, or even frost heave.

Mossie, in his capacity as honorary grain consultant, says a lot of things that are unprintable about it being my fault for using home-saved seed. He says that's alright for barley and rape, but a disaster for wheat. Apparently we need to get stuff from the south because it has been longer in the bag to get over its dormancy. The only hope of the four tonne harvest lies in tillering. The fine weather will be helping and so will the nitrogen. It'll get more every time the sun shines.

When it is dry enough we'll roll the park - and here's a tip. Buy shares in Cycocel. We'll be putting it on the wheat this year - with a shovel.

Rastus not clicking with girls

THE CALVING has got off to an early start - and one which has left me very puzzled.

You will recall that in the spring I bought a fine Aberdeen-Angus bull called Rastus. The theory was that, as the 30 Black Hereford heifers were to calve before they were two years old, a Black bull would be just the thing to give them a nice wee calf for a start.

Rastus took his jacket off on June 1, so his calves should be due as from about March 15. We are looking forward to a deluge of vital little black calves. No doubt we'll get them, but the calving has started and we already have one little bull. But there is nothing black about him. He is white, and that unmistakable chocolate colour that comes from the Simmental.

I was baffled by that because Argus, the Simmental bull, had been in strict training, along with Rastus, as he prepared for his work among the mature cows.

I eventually solved the mystery by reference to a Farmer's Diary I wrote in early June last year. In it, I told you that Rastus was making a middling job of the bulling. That was not my view, but seemed to reflect the opinion of the heifers. I had seen three of them, all in heat or at least getting warm, who had forsaken Rastus and jumped the dyke to the next field to play with a beautiful little Simmental bull who was still suckling his mother, being only eight months old.

Now, it is obvious, I hope, that the change from the planned sire wouldn't make the calf come any earlier. Indeed, Simmental calves should be three days or so later. So how does this solve the mystery?

It doesn't, but it does give rise to a hypothesis. You see, one of the remarkable things about those goings-on was that, after they had had their fun, the heifers jumped back in beside Rastus. So maybe this had been going on for a couple of months before Rastus even arrived in the field. It

may have been a regular relationship rather than a spur of the moment affair.

I wasn't pleased last year when I discovered that the little bull was serving the heifers, and I had a session with Big Hamish about it when we met for our usual discussion group at the Salmon Inn that Sunday. Hamish said it would be alright. As the bull was only seven hundred-weight at the most, any resulting pregnancies would result in very small calves and the heifers would get easy calvings.

"No, no, Hamish," said I, delighted to have caught the big man out again. "You see, it isn't the actual size of a bull that determines the size of a calf. It's the genetic size, and that bull is the biggest breed in the country and, accordingly that will lead to a big calf. Oh, yes. We could have a couple of stiff calvings there."

Now Hamish may not have a degree in biology, but he knows when he's being patronised. "Right oh, then," he said defiantly. "We'll jist wait and see fa's richt in the spring time."

It was on Saturday morning. I had had a long lie, and dawn was breaking when I staggered to the window to sniff the weather. In the first light of a rhymie morning I saw a couple of the heifers running down to the bottom of the field and peering excitedly over the fence.

I hadn't heard it myself, but I was sure they had been attracted by the roar that often accompanies the last great heave when a calf is born, and sometimes means that a life and death struggle has been joined.

I dressed quickly and ran outside. I loaded the cart with the American calf puller, the ropes, halters, and the pinch bar for turning calves that have stuck. All that might have taken ten minutes which might have been precious. But they had not been.

When I got down to the field my heifer, still two months short of her second birthday, was suckling a fine wee bull calf. Big Hamish, while quite wrong scientifically, was quite right in this case, and this was the case in point. I don't think I'll tell him.

Now, we bought the black bull because of his reputation for giving small lively calves, which bounce up and suck as soon as they are born. We suspect the Simmentals of producing a high proportion of big lazy brutes of calves which are hard to get out and are slow to suck. But this calf was perfect.

So what about the little bull who performed so manfully while only seven months old? Should he not be given a chance to do the business professionally? I have found him down in what used to be the barley-beef shed where we are fattening a few males. He is intact, and looking very pretty. He has a gorgeous curly light brown and white coat, four good legs, and a roast on him that would make the mouth water. So I could make a bull of him. It will certainly be tempting if my heifers produce many more Simmental calves like the first one.

On the other hand, he's quite small for a bull. At sixteen months old I don't think he is twelve hundredweight. And then again, he would be a good trade at Maud, and the beef market is going like a fair at the moment so I'll likely obey the old law of selling fat cattle: *"If you've got fat cattle sell them when they're fat."*

169

Silly me sprayed the wrong park

I DON'T see what they are all laughing about. There is nothing funny in it that I can see. It cost me a lot of money - money right down the tube - and in these straightened times, that seems very unfunny. Still, if the boys in the discussion group think it's funny maybe you will too - so here goes.

It was a perfectly understandable mistake which anybody could have made. In fact, it happened once before at Little Ardo. That was in the days when we got the Chemical Spraying Company to put on the environmenticides. The job was to spray a field of wheat for knot grass.

Unfortunately the orders were not clear enough and the sprayer went in at the wrong gate. He was once round the field before he noticed that the field looked more like new grass than wheat, and stopped to seek new orders. He fairly got them and I was able to extract a very favourable deal from his employers.

Now that WAS funny. But this time I was in the sprayer, I was the employer and there was nowhere to go for the compensation.

You see the finest brains in Aberdeenshire are currently engaged in devising schemes to frustrate the EEC's attempts to make us reduce output by setting aside 15 percent of our cereal acres. I need hardly say that those finest brains belong to the Grain Barons, Mossie and the Red Rooster. They believe set-aside will reward us with a tremendous run of wheat if we use it as a break crop.

And the key to that great crop is a specially designed chemical potion to be applied in exact proportions, at exactly the right time, and at huge expense.

So that was my job last week. The exactly right amount of the cocktail arrived in unmarked oil drums. The sprayer was greased and filled. I was ready for the off.

And then Potions arrived, all bright-eyed as usual. I blame him for my accident.

"What are you doing with the bales that are still lying

about in the bottom field?" he asked. Well, I didn't like to admit that I hadn't given the matter one moment's thought so I improvised. "I'll jist spray roon them. It'll mak nae difference for a few bales."

But that wasn't good enough for Potions. "You should get the Wasting Asset to take the digger down and shift them onto the bit you've sprayed and that way you'll get it all covered properly." Fair enough, though I couldn't see that it was any business of his, that was what I would do.

And it was done.

I was on my last round when I noticed, in the field next to the one I was spraying, the field next to the one Potions had made me shift those bales around, that there was a nice green show of aftermath.

Now, as you know, I am outwintering some 30 heifers which are due to calve in mid March. They are starving away on a diet of mud augmented by straw and three pounds of cobs a day. "Why don't I open the gate and let the heifers get that nice green bite,' said I to myself.

And then, "Silly-me! That's my set-aside. I'm not allowed to let the cattle graze the set-aside. SET-ASIDE! But I'm supposed to be spraying my set-aside." That was indeed my set-aside and I was just finishing spraying the wrong park.

There is nothing farmers like better than to dwell on the misfortunes of their neigh-

171

bours so I was now in a position to make all mine very happy indeed. But I had a selfish disinclination to do so.

I would have liked to say nothing but I was trapped. How was I to get some more of the magic brew if I didn't at least own up to the grand wizard. And telling him would hardly be less effective than getting it on the BBC.

The guru of grain growers was sounding unusually depressed when I phoned. There was nothing to do. The pigs had all been cleared out prior to going 'high health', the baby was asleep, the kids were at school, none of his pals were answering their phones and harvest seemed a long time away.

I started casually. I talked about the weather, his health, and the family. Then nonchalantly, as if in afterthought, I said, "Oh, and I'll need another eleven acres of the magic brew."

I could feel the hot glow of delight pulsating along the telephone line. All the depression left him in one glorious moment of concentrated malice, "You've sprayed the wrang park!" he crowed.

It mattered not how often I explained about it all being Potion's fault or how it could happen to anyone. "Oh you're in front Charlie. You've daen next year's sprayin aaready. What a boy tae get on wi the job! Ha, ha ha."

Ha, ha, indeed.

He told me where to get the stuff. I could collect it when I liked, and, no, he wouldn't be there when I arrived.

He didn't need to tell me where he would be. I knew. He would be off down to the pub to tell anybody that would listen (and there would be plenty of them) about the park that got its set-aside spray a year early.

I'm playing it cool though. I'm not beat yet. If I had another sixty-two acres I could plough up for linseed I'd need another eleven acres of set-aside and could set the field I sprayed aside after all. With all the white settlers about here it shouldn't be that difficult to get another field or two.

I could show them all yet.

Bovines have come up trumps

IF WE farmers don't keep telling everyone we're on the verge of ruin, they will think we are in clover. It is politic for us to keep up the storm of complaints so that THEY will keep up our subsidies. And, anyway, people expect farmers to be pleading poverty all the time. In a rapidly changing world, farmers driving huge cars to the banks with tears in their eyes is something to hold on to.

For all that, I have to break ranks.

Things are looking bad for employment on the land. With all this set-aside there would be bound to be even less to do, even if we weren't saving labour at the usual alarming rate. The potato producers who have to take £10 a tonne are undoubtedly hurting, and the hill sheep men may be finding their row harder to hoe than sometimes but, for a farmer like me, things are looking good, or at least well above average.

All the combinable crops are at prices that promise a profit. If wheat and barley stay up near the levels indicated by the futures markets, we should have no difficulty in grossing £400 an acre, and the EEC is going to give us an acreage payment as well. Against all expectation, rape seed has risen to £140 a tonne and the wise people in Brussels have reacted to that by raising the subsidy for sowing the stuff to over £200. If we have any odd bit of scrub or heath into which a plough can be forced, the Eurocracy will pay us £250 or so just to sow linseed. Whatever they say, there is no need to do anything to the crop. You don't even have to harvest it.

And then there is set-aside. I don't like it much but, unless I had enormous overheads, it would be impossible to go broke getting something for nothing.

All that has been known for some time. But the blot on my normal horizon is the cattle. Lovely as they are, they have been stiff to make pay. Mossie never misses the chance to call me 'the workin feel' for bothering with them.

He's right, of course, but now even the bovines have come up smelling of roses. I sold seventeen of them last week and what a pleasure - nay, a treat - that was.

It was mostly odds and sods, like the twin Simmental bulls that I had not cut on the off-chance that someone would need them for service. With the grazing season approaching I didn't want just two bulls to keep inside. They were early spring calves last year and I took them to be over eight hundredweight. Down they went to the weekly sale of young bulls at Thainstone and there they gave me one of life's pleasant little surprises.

They were nearer half a tonne and sold to 137 pence a kilo - my best price ever. They came to £1320 for the produce of one old Simmental cow. The best is that she has calved again early and it is another brace, though this time one is a heifer.

As you know, I am not one to blow about my successes, but I couldn't help but share my joy with my friend Jackie Gallagher, an Irish cattle dealer of seventy summers and about a hundred winters.

He was visibly moved. "Char-Les," he said in that peculiar way of his, "go home and be as good to that cow as if she had been your own mother."

What he meant was that I

should be as good to that cow as I wish I had been to my own mother - and I will.

And the twins weren't even my second best sale. That was the three older bulls I consigned straight to the slaughterhouse.They really were a rum crew. They included another failed breeding bull which made £843. Then there was the cross-country bull which last summer cleared every hedge and dyke in the district to my acute embarrassment. He made £820. But the best was surely the last of my Jersey crosses. He achieved the stunning grade of 'O minus' and realised a staggering £631, more than twice what I had paid for his mother.

I also sold ten heifers that I'd looked at long enough. Being a subsidy junkie and the male chauvinistic Euro-pigs having put all the subsidy on the males, there seemed little point in looking at them any longer.

They sold to a top of 128 pence a kilo for three Simmental cross Black Herefords. As those are what I aim to produce once I have bred the Jersey out, that was encouraging.

But it wasn't half as encouraging as the sale of the screws. There were two among the ten heifers. One had lost its mother and had survived by theft. It was a Jersey cross and only just survived the loss of its mother, but, like the Artful Dodger, it became proficient in crime and was now driving me nuts by stealing the milk from a new generation of calves. The other screw was bigger but also had the Channel Island blood which meant it was ideally built for jumping in and out through angle barriers. It was therefore able to feed royally all winter on the feed which the others were supposed to get the next day.

Those two ranagles averaged 340 kilos and made £380 - surely my best sale of the day.

As I left the box I was attacked by one of those pests of whom Aberdeenshire has been more or less rid, the determined luck-penny seeker. My defences were well up, "Which did you buy," I asked as grippily as I might. But when he replied, "the last two" I had the greatest pleasure in giving him two pounds along with my heartfelt wishes for the very best of luck.

It had been a good sale, well summed up by Jackie Gallagher, "Better a seller than a buyer be," he said gravely.

Mornings belong to the geese

I HAVE been enjoying the lightening mornings. It is my pleasure to sit with a cup of tea at my office window and watch a new dawn dawning and a new spring springing.

There is no shortage of things to see between six and seven.

There is a fox which patrols across the field in front of the house. It doesn't just trot past. Nose down, it casts back and fore enjoying or trying to understand some scent or other. I expect it will one day get some of the young of the partridges which seem set to nest in the rape. I'll be sad at that for I have always had a soft spot for partridges.

The foxes are welcome to a few pheasants though. I know they have been here longer than my family but they still seem gaudy exotics - whereas the 'pairtricks' are like hardy natives.

There are three roe deer which I see some mornings. They spend their time moving from a den near the Salmon Inn about a mile and a half to the little wood which lies between the farm and the village of Methlick.

What are they doing? Three seems an awkward number as the breeding season approaches. Are they looking for a fourth? Should they not cast their net a bit wider. Do they not realise that they have already looked in the den and in the wood for half the winter and not found another?

But the mornings really belong to the geese. It is a funny thing about Little Ardo but, fine stock farm though it is, the geese don't like it. Up till this year I have only once seen geese land here. That was during a very hard winter when we had a burst drain which produced a bit of green in the frozen wilderness. And yet, on three successive mornings, about a dozen geese have tried our set-aside this year. They couldn't have liked it either for they have not been back.

The geese pass Little Ardo on the way to greener pastures where they are welcomed only by the hunters

176

and, if sport it be, those must have a lot of sport. There are thousands and thousands of geese and I am in their flight path. In the early mornings they fly straight at me as they come across the valley from the lakes at Haddo House. Often they seem to gain just enough height to avoid flying right in at the office window.

This morning I made an attempt to count them. I found that sixty made a small skein. At the busiest there were perhaps ten of those strung across the valley, and the waves of birds carried on for 45 seconds. As they fly at over thirty miles an hour they must have been about half a mile deep. Five thousand birds would have been a genuine guess, though probably not a very good one.

Sitting at this window, where five generations of my family have sat, has stirred in me once more the sense of place I have here. No doubt my great grandfather, John Yull the auctioneer, sat here recovering. He used to lead the fun after the marts, drink more than would be good for a normal man, and then bet that he could beat the fastest runner carrying the heaviest reveller on his back. He got a start, of course, but the story goes that he never lost such a bet. John Yull would then drink a good deal more, and then be driven home as he slept by his good horse Clatterin Jean.

I love the old stories like that. And my sense of history was raised to new heights by what happened on Monday.

I was just finishing my dinner when I had a phone call to the effect that I had four minutes to wash, shave, dress and drive twenty-four miles to address the Peterhead Rotary club. That would not have been a generous allowance of time even if the Jaguar's battery had not been flat and even if my mother's gravestone had not been in the back of the only other car available.

It may seem eccentric to carry your mother's gravestone around in your second best car, but I had just been up to the quarry to get the sandstone she so admired. She thought it doucer than the local granite.

Anyway, I was making rapid progress despite the additional weight, when I approached a halt sign at the bottom of a steepish hill. The car would have been hard put to it to stop without a five hundredweight block of Morayshire pushing. It was immediately clear that there was no way I was going to stop.

Summoning all that re-

mains of the strength that once let me toss the caber for Scotland, I jammed my foot to the floor and burst the oil pipe.

And there's more.

The need for a new stone arises from congestion in the family grave in the kirkyard in Methlick. My mother decided we should start on the plot next to where John Yull lies. It had been bought with remarkable foresight after a particularly good harvest but had so far remained empty. Mum's in there now. So is Dad and, in the fullness of time, I will follow.

So the stone which was hurtling behind me towards the road junction wasn't just my mother's but my own.

My whole life did not flash past me. I just imagined the newspaper headline, "Farmer killed by own gravestone".

But I didn't hit anything on the crossroads. I couldn't get off the road for the high banks but I was able to take some of the pace off the old car by ramming her into the side a couple of times. Luckily there was nothing coming and I just managed to scrape round the bend at the bottom of the hill.

The rotary lads were very understanding about my being late but thought I seemed a bit nervous.

The Yank blanched at £25,000

IT IS said - and I have good reason to believe it, because I was closely involved with that first importation - that an American paid the price of a small farm for three Chianina heifers when they first arrived in Britain.

They are the tallest and among the heaviest cattle in the world so, in 1973, when we first imported them, there was a queue of stetson hats wanting to buy the progeny for export to the land of milk and money. They were all most welcome visitors, but no other was so welcome as the man who appeared at the farm of one of the finest breeders of Scotland's traditional cattle. I shall call him Bill Tosh.

Now, the dollar signs that accompanied them from Italy were the only things Bill liked about the Chianinas. They were far too tall for a market that was just being weaned off Bill's own philosophy that 'a beef animal should have a flat back, a flat belly and be as close to the ground as possible'.

The new cattle went to over six feet tall at the tail head and were up to a foot lower in the smalls of their backs.

When, about two years later, I put the first of the Chianina crosses through the ring at Maud, she was bought by John Mackintosh, the butcher. He paid me a good enough price but when I asked him the following week how the heifer had killed out he said, "Like an effing cricket bat."

The Chianinas look well between the shafts though. I thought them particularly beautiful with a red rose stuck on their foreheads when I saw them shown in Italy. They were the original draft animals which pulled the carts which brought the Christians into the rings to feed the lions in ancient Rome.

But Bill Tosh had more sense of value than of history. He was delighted therefore when the stetson appeared in his close. The heifers had cost him £3000 which twenty years ago was even more money than it is today. Bill thought he should give himself a bit of a margin for profit and leeway in negotiation, so, when the conversation got round to specifics, he asked £25,000 for the three heifers.

The American blanched, said it was rather more than he had expected to pay, phoned his partner in America and agreed to Bill's price.

Bill knew he had a bargain but he didn't realise just how good until it came time for payment. The stetson wrote out a cheque, not for £25,000 - but for £75,000. He had been dealing on a per-head basis whereas Bill was selling the whole pen.

This will undoubtedly astonish you, but Bill never alerted the American to his mistake. He accepted his good fortune as just reward for his labour and due recompense for all the times he had missed out.

I have told you all that because I have just had it brought home to me how far we have moved since the heady days when buyers beat a path to our doors, looking for exotic cattle.

You see, I also had some of the first Simmental cattle into the country. I had heifers from Germany, France and Austria.

That started in 1970 when we paid £400 for four from Germany. I went to see that far-seeing and knowledge-able chap, the village banker, seeking finance for the project. "How much? Four hundred pounds apiece? Oh, na, na Charlie. I canna advise extravagance like that."

I had to change banks to

get the money.

And yet we sold the first batch of calves for £2,500 each.

And things improved even further. I was stupid enough to fancy keeping a heifer of the second calves. She was not for sale at any price.

Then a group from Australia pestered me into naming a price. Without the slightest fear that they would accept I said, "Ten thousand", and when that didn't stop them I said, "guineas."

It was all nonsense, of course. It couldn't last and it didn't.

But it has taken until now for the price to get right down to what the pure Simmentals are worth as commercial beasts.

The first step was when we cut our first pure bull. Then we sold a few bulls without trying to halter them or give them any fancy feeding for the sale.

And now we have taken the final leap towards treating our exotics as commercial cattle.

I had a pure heifer calved today. She is light in colour and deep bodied with a very pretty face. She reminds me in every way except financially, of my 10,000gn. heifer. Yet her calf is dark chocolate in colour and is after the Aberdeen Angus bull. She was a bit young but I didn't want to leave her a whole year so I put her in with Rastus the Black bull who was attending to the Black-Hereford heifers.

She's the first to calve to Rastus - and the signs are good. The calf is tall and well set up with every chance that she may prove to be a grower with a good back-end.

But with the best luck in the world she's not worth more than £200. And yet her auntie, the one that went to Australia, made 10,000gns twenty years ago.

March 29, 1993

Kilmarnock bunnet gets a blasting

THERE IS a truly horrible part of my life and today I want to tell you how the spring calves, which are arriving thick and fast, are helping me to cope.

The low point is when daylight and the senses return after a night out with the boys who will still be boys though it is long since they became men. There is the gradual piecing together of all that went on, or came off, the night before. There is the checking of the old bones to make sure that none is broken and that the arthritic knees are not any worse than is to be expected. There is the sandpaper at the back of the throat and the relentless woodpeckers which have somehow got inside the skull and are prospecting for the softest bit through which to tunnel to freedom. Usually they try the hard bit underneath the eyebrows, but, every now and then, they try the soft bit at the back of the eyes sending shocks along the painways of this ageing body.

From long experience of this condition I know how to deal with it. You see, it lasts until the first bit of hard work has been done and the second mug of tea has been drunk. Lie there in bed and you will be half conscious but in agony all morning. But, if you get up, force down the first mug of tea, charge round the farm working furiously for an hour and then have another mugful, recovery will be all but complete before most of the world is awake.

Now, it is all very well to know that you should get on with it, if you want to recover, but unless there is something desperately needing done it is easy just to lie there being miserable.

And that is where the calvings come in. We are expecting something like fifty calves in forty-two days - so there is always something that just must be got up for. I've already found two cows with dead calves hanging out of them, despite looking at them last thing at night and at first light, so I just have to tackle the hangovers head-

182

on.

I was in dire need of that sort of discipline last weekend, for Mossie and his pal, Nicol from Keith, had a party. The deal was: drinks at one-thirty p.m.; clay pigeon shooting at three followed by beef done in Mossie's mobile rotisseri (the one he made by converting his old muck-spreader); presentation of prizes and more jollity until ten. That was when the wives were invited to join us for a drink in case any of the boys needed a run home. Oh no. We don't forget the ladies.

I was pleased at the prospect of the party despite my fears for Sunday morning. For one thing it would mean I couldn't watch the English giving the hapless Irish a walloping in the rugby match in Dublin. (In fact the Irish won handsomely but I wasn't to know that.) But I did ask Mossie if he was sure we could get away with such a party in this day and age when women were harbouring aspirations about a fair deal and even being militantly feminine.

The great barley baron had clearly given that one a lot of thought. "Oh, no." he said. "This is Aberdeenshire. We're nae much bothered wi that kind o thing here. And onyway, my wife doesna like sheetin."

Neither does mine but then she hasn't tried it. Indeed when it comes to shooting clay doos, neither had I until the party.

And after the party I don't have any reason to anticipate a great future as a clay-pigeon shooter.

It turns out that there are all sorts of mysteries to be unravelled. Like, it is no use saying, "I'm ready," or Right," or even "C'mon an boys, fire the gun among the geese." It is part of the free-masonry of clay-doo shooting that they won't fire the clay until you say "pull".

Now, I knew that I'd be out of my depth among such dedicated shooters so, to do all I could for my image, I decided to yoke the Jaguar and wear my magnificent Kilmarnock bonnet. The lady who gave me that said it was wide enough to land a helicopter on, and she was only half joking. Certainly it would have given a comfortable roost to at least twenty sparrows.

Anyway, as there was to be something called 'high birds', I was advised to take off my bonnet, in case I couldn't see for the wide rim.

But therein lay my big mistake. When I was failing to say the right word to get

my first bird launched I eventually exclaimed as the tension mounted, "For god's sake, boys. What are ye waitin for?" Whereupon a huge black shape was launched from behind me and came skimming over my head. Quick as a flash, I had my gun up and gave it both barrels. It was just about my only kill all day. I suppose I could hardly have missed so big a target, but it will never be a Sunday bonnet again.

I didn't see who threw it, but, if he's any man at all, he'll be in the market for a new Kilmarnock.

I didn't get a blank card, though. Not quite. It was decided that, as I was down to present the prizes, it would be too embarrassing if I won the booby, so three were added to my score. That left me only forty-one birds behind Keith Johnstone, the grain merchant who, not content with skinning us in the market, went off with the handsome trophy and the champagne.

There were a lot of prizes but my favourite award was for the best-dressed shot. That went to councillor Jock Robertson, a publican who had the savoir faire to come with a deep red carnation in his buttonhole. Jock is a legend in his lunchtime hereabouts, not least for his immortal remark, "Ye ken, boys. If I had only kent I wis gaun tae live sae lang I'd of taen better care o masel."

Anyway, the party turned out to be a twelve hour affair,

so I was glad of the excuse that I would have to leave so that I could look round my calvers. I needn't have bothered. Four of them had managed without me.

Troubles come in threes

IT IS not superstition. I believe that bad events come in threes because I have observed that it is so.

As we are in the middle of the calving this is a particularly messy time to have bad events and on Saturday night we had them.

The night started off well enough with a trip to Aberdeen to see the Buddy Holly story which turned out to be no more than some of the songs of our courting days well sung and danced, and strung together with some of the worst acting of the most puerile dialogue I have ever heard.

We had dinner before the second house, so by the time we got home it was pushing one o'clock. If I had left it at that I would have closed the door on British Winter Time in mellow mood.

But The Farmer would have a last look round his cows. It's been so dry that I can get the old Cavalier into the field and there I found her.

She was calving all right. I could see the two feet sticking out...would this be a bull calf? In the most shocking piece of male chauvinism I know, the EEC gives all the subbie money to the bull calves and none to the heifers and we've had sixty percent heifers so far.

Now this was to be another Aberdeen-Angus calf after our black bull Rastus (unless she had jumped in beside the Simmental calf like three of her sisters) and really they had been plopping out quite easily and usually unseen.

Certainly unseen was how she wanted it for I couldn't get near enough to help had such been needed. I decided to try the bed.

But I was uneasy about my cow. I didn't like the set of the calf's legs. Something seemed wrong. After an hour of trying I got up at what was three o'clock because of the time change.

The heifer was still not calved. She was trying hard but the legs were sticking nearly a foot out and still no sign of a nose.

Now she was getting tired and she let me get a hand in. I always get a boost when I'm fretting over a cow calving when I can get a finger into the calf's mouth and feel the movement of the tongue. But this time I got a surprise. There was no tongue but a tail. I had a calf which was erse-for-elbow, or, as the vet put it, "a posterior presentation".

Now I've pulled out hundreds of calves but, very strangely, for it is not a very uncommon thing, I haven't had a posterior presentation before, so I decided to make that the excuse for calling the vet. Why, after all, if I was up at three-thirty, should he not be also.

While I was making up my mind to share the misery of that morning, I noticed in the sweep of the headlights another cow some hundred yards away. She was jumping to her feet and wheeling round in that unmistakable way of cows who have successfully delivered themselves. And sure enough. She had a calf. A bull calf too which put me in better fettle.

Despite her twice running right through me to get to where her waters had burst, I had got the heifer in by four o'clock. I had phoned the vet, made a cup of tea and was looking forward to my two calves in the morning.

The vet tried to pull the

calf out with his pogo stick but pronounced it stuck fast. It would have to be a Caesarean. Fine. What's a hundred pounds when the first subby on bull calves is fifty-four pounds and stores are at a hundred and forty pence a kilo?

We got her shaved and anaesthetised and the floor swept. As he made his first deep incision the vet put the deal in perspective. "You know," he said, "if this was a human it would just be a death for sure."

And yet we knew the cow was in no danger.

Soon I had my second bull calf of the night - stone dead. Now the operation started to look dearer. And Rastus, the bull bought for the smallness of his calves, started to look dearer too.

Within ten minutes the cow was up and eating silage. A wee bit unsteady but none the worse.

It being now half past six I thought I'd cheer myself up by looking at the calf which had been born so easily in the field. I knew he'd be fine but it was just an excuse to see the good news.

There was no good news.

The calf was flat out.

It wasn't dead though. Unless I'm mistaken it was worse than that. The calf was spastic. He was full of life but had no control over it. His attempts to get up and suck resulted in him arching his back and putting his head right back so that it was lying along his back. I sat him up but he just collapsed immediately and stretched back as though trying to get at an udder somewhere behind him.

By the time I had thawed out some collostrum, fed him and tumbled into bed, it was half past seven.

Now you must never think that just because your barn has blown down and your grain drier caught fire that the wife won't have forgotten to post the insurance money.

It was just before eight that the Wasting Asset phoned. Poor boy. He had had a hellova night out on the town and was stranded in Aberdeen. Would I mind feeding the beasts?

Who? Me?

I will sleep all the better once they are done. You see his call was the third disaster.

Going through a bad patch

AFTER MY three disasters last week I had hoped to have nothing but good news for you this week, but the truth will out. It's not all fun being a stock farmer at calving time.

The fourth disaster was an old cow which had had a fine Charolais cross calf. I wanted to move her and another newly calved cow from the group of expectant ladies to another bunch which had calved and were getting a rather better diet. This was done and all seemed to be well, including the usual excited milling around and snorting that happens when you mix cattle.

Now, the accommodation to which the old dears were being moved has long been regarded as first rate for wintering cattle and absolutely useless for anything else. There are two sheds, the old barn built by my great-great-grandfather, William Yull, in 1857, and the old byre which is probably eighteenth century and has virtually no chance of making the twenty-first. I remember, about 1946, one of the dairy cattleman's sons crashing to the floor in a cloud of dust, the last time anybody tried to climb along the couples (rafters).

The cattle are fed silage in the old barn, concentrates in a trough in the midden and they usually choose, in all but the worst weather, to rest on the dung heap though they have the freedom to roam the two sheds.

Well, now, in the excitement of moving two new cows and calves into this salubrious accommodation, one old dear somehow went down in a particularly soft bit of the muck. She was quite stuck and I had to get the digger and make her an escape route. It took her a couple of hours to rise but by nightfall all was well.

Or so I thought. The next morning she couldn't rise. Despite taking her out to the field on the digger and hoisting her up every day with a thing that grabbed her by the hurdies, she has had to be destroyed, leaving a calf to be

189

fostered.

The hoist did work with the young heifer which couldn't rise after her calving. We think her calf had been dead as it did not have the thickening of the tongue which happens if the calf has a long struggle to win free. Anyway I got her on my early morning round with the calf half out. It came out easily but after it came the womb.

That is a horrendous business though it doesn't seem to distress the cows much. Luckily I was there when it was happening and I caught it half out and with a struggle got the calf bed shoved back in. When he came the vet stitched it in to make sure.

And there's more.

The vet said the spastic calf, which could not hold his head still let alone rise to his feet and suck, might not be spastic but have brain damage and might respond to nursing. We should take milk off his mother and feed it to him through a pipe.

And again, another of the heifers has a calf which has a defect in its mouth. This has the effect that when it should be sucking it blows. Twice a day, with the help of the Wasting Asset, I force the teat into her mouth. All she has to do is stick her tongue underneath it and suck. But what she does is to stick her tongue underneath it and spit.

Oh boys! I'm going through a bad patch.

But, as always, hope springs.

The spastic calf surprised me. There was only one thing it could do but that was suck. So all we had to do was to get a small bale of straw and put that underneath him and hold him onto the teat. Thank goodness he had a totally patient mother who had plenty of milk. We still have to feed him but that calf can now stand for short spells himself though he can't yet hold his head in the right position to suckle.

While the spastic is feeding we can steal enough to feed the one that can't suck. We are giving her enough to keep her alive but not so much that she losses the will to try. Though she is fighting fit she is making no headway yet and her mother, who had no milk anyway, absconded back to the field without her.

The calf of the cow we had to put down is away with the heifer that had her calf bed out and both seem happy about life together.

And while this is going on, the oilseed rape which has only had one spray is looking really well as is the winter barley, which can hardly help but leave us something like five hundred pounds an acre at harvest time. Three fields of wheat are looking fine but one is looking poor. Mossie and I had a tour round the crops the other day. He thinks I should sow spring barley through the bad park. "That'll give you the option," he says. "If wheat's a big price call it wheat and if there is a good trade for barley that's what you sell it as."

He's right, of course, cattle are a poor crop compared with the work involved. But when summer comes and he's lying in bed dreaming of his acreage payments, I'll be going round my cows and calves. I've got thirty-five already and by that time they'll be a show.

191

Mother and daughter get together again

Now here's a tale to warm the cockles of the coldest heart. Even grain barons, who can never get such joy from their green and yellow fields no matter how high the acreage payments go, are bound to be touched.

I am pleased to be able to tell you that the calving is going better. We have forty on the ground now and even the problems are resolving themselves. The spastic calf which could only lie flat on the ground and suck is making remarkable progress. We started by tying his mother up, setting a small bale of straw under him and holding him on to the teat.

Then we threw away the bale and he managed to stand though he couldn't balance nor could he take the teat himself nor could he hold his head still. Then after a few days he started to take the teat himself though he needed to be put in about and held steady.

And there is more progress today. After his second feed I left him after he had been free-standing for a full minute and a half. It seems he can now stand but only his back legs can walk. That has obvious disadvantages. When he tries to move, his back legs quickly overtake the front ones and he falls in a most uncomfortable heap.

Nevertheless, he seems to be winning. But the star turn is the calf who when she should have been sucking would only blow. If we put the teat into her mouth she would make the frantic motions which usually lead to milk production but in this calf's case only led to the spitting-out of the teat.

I told you last time that the mother had abandoned her calf and run away back to her field. It really didn't matter as she appeared to have no milk anyway and, if the calf was going to be so difficult to feed, we were better using the spastic calf's mum as she is a wonderfully patient and milky dame. I had also thought that, when the spastic died, we would be able to solve two problems at once.

Three times a day we hauled her in about to her foster mother, squirted milk into her mouth and stuck the teat in. Every time she spat it out. We would give up after a while and take a couple of pints off and put it straight into her stomach. The natural mother seemed quite unconcerned and as dry as a cricket bat.

But then a queer thing happened.

When the calf was about five days old I went down to the shed to restart the farcical struggle but found her gone. It would be easy for her to escape as all she had to do was to walk through an angle barrier. My strategy on such occasions is not to panic but to continue with my rounds. The missing calves have a habit of emerging. And so it was on this occasion.

I found the calf at the roadside halfway down to the field to which her mother had absconded. The mother had apparently jumped the gate and met her calf halfway. What signalling method they used to communicate over half a mile I don't know but it wasn't the normal bellowing, for I have sensitive ears when it comes to cows bellowing in the night. She had still no great appearance of milk but the calf was round and full and its nose was a little furnace.

The calf could suck all right, she had just been

193

waiting for the right stuff. Whether the cow and calf would have got it together had I just left them to it I cannot tell but calves cannot normally survive to day five without the mother's first milk. On the other hand, if I'd kept out of the way, she might not have had to.

And my travails with the calves led me to another sweet sight this week. After a very dry winter we have now been blessed with far too much rain. The fields which have supported cattle all winter with remarkably little damage have turned quickly to brown and the cattle have headed for the high ground - especially the calves.

I've been feeding their mums silage and straw and I must confess that I haven't been very fussy about taking off the wrappings, which has led to a build up in the feed rings. Yesterday when I looked out there were five calves, sound asleep on the unsavoury tangle of rejected straw, black plastic, net and string - two feet clear of the flood.

At any rate the calving is sorting itself out. It is being a bit of a scramble but I now have forty calves which is the number of cows for which I have applied for quota. Any more, and there will be a few, will be a bonus. And, if I can get a bit of beef on them, there will be a further big bonus from selling those cows which are empty or very late, for the trade is excellent just now.

But I'm not looking forward to next week. I must fill in those damned forms and I just cannot see how I can possibly get away with it. After all, I'm the man who was fined for overdeclaring my rape acreages last time, despite trying to play safe. And last time I also had the greatest difficulty over my HLCA payments. I had the right number of cows alright but I couldn't explain how I got from last year's number to this year's so I was fined one cow's worth.

With my record they are bound to be watching me. I just have a sinking feeling about the whole deal.

April 26, 1993

Infallible signs of Spring

There is a story which has been around in our family for long enough for me to have forgotten exactly who was involved, but I remember the circumstances quite well. I tell it because it illustrates something about the difference between people here on Scotland's cold shoulder, and people in Glasgow. Or maybe it's the difference between country folk and townies everywhere.

It concerns a grieve at an out-farm in Aberdeenshire. Spring was threatening to leap out once again and he required a couple of hundred fencing posts against the free-range cow. Having got the farmer to agree to send up two hundred four-foot-six posts the grieve closed the conversation with, "Be sure and get larch. Pine posts are awfu sparkie in the fire."

Now, in the sixties when I lived in Glasgow, I made the mistake of trying that story on some friends. They misunderstood the point altogether. To a person, they thought the point was that the men on the

farm would be stealing the posts for the fire - that would be why they wanted good burning sticks.

But that wasn't what the story was about at all. It illustrated the quality of forward planning that you got from the old-fashioned grieve.

He was thinking ahead. With luck that fence might last twenty-five years. Then it would have to be replaced. Then, and only then, would the men on the farm get a few posts each to saw up for the fire. The grieve was thinking twenty-five years ahead. He might have retired or even be pushing up daisies, but he wanted whoever was around to have logs that wouldn't send sparks out onto the kitchen rug.

I was reminded of that by the fact that Spring is here. I know it's Spring-time because of two infallible signs. The silage is finished and the first lot of cows have broken out and gone trampling through the garden. The Breadwinner's carefully tended beds have now got

195

great plod marks all over them and the greens, so carefully manicured all last summer and nursed back to perfection after last spring's invasion, have now got what look like so many golf holes all over them.

There is a lot to be said for the dark nights when the Breadwinner (who is away all day winning bread) can't see what's all gone wrong.

Like the Wasting Asset cowping the digger.

He was taking the last of the silage in out of the park, deep-rutted after a winter of running in and out. It would have been a hazardous journey at the best of times but really the Asset gave himself no chance. He had only three toes of the grape in the bale which meant half a tonne of silage was trying to tip the digger over. That it did just as soon as he hit a deep rut.

Now it has to be said that my new digger has been a big disappointment to me. It hasn't been home a year and it has got a wonkie torque, the diff. lock has shattered, and the engine has seized. So when I saw it lying on its side my first instinct was to get a new digger and cover it over.

In fact I couldn't see how we were going to get it on its feet anyway. I'd have liked to do it myself so that I could keep the truth from my neighbours, but the only method I could think of was to put a chain over the top and haul. That would have shattered the safety cab.

It was at a considerable sacrifice of face that I decided to ask Big Hamish to come with his fancy digger. I did ask him not to tell anyone but I might as well have told the BBC. He arrived with Mossie, Crookie, Hilly and the Red Rooster, called on his mobile phone, as well as a few people he'd met on the way over. "Charlie's cowpit's digger. C'mon and see the fun."

Hamish may be struggling with the mysteries surrounding the percent and some other details that he missed at school, but there's no denying him when it comes to driving a digger. It was disappointingly easy really. He just put a chain round a bit of the axle and onto the toes of his great bucket and pulled the old dear onto her feet by tipping the bucket.

"Aye, you're going through a bad patch," said Mossie, but you could see he was disappointed.

And I am going through a bad patch.

I've had to sack the Wasting Asset. It wasn't anything to do with cowping the dig-

196

ger. The job really didn't suit him; it was interfering with his social life which made an eight o'clock start on a Monday an unattainable dream.

The relationship between father and son is often a difficult one and I'm sure it gets more difficult the older the relatives get. He may well find it easier to work to a stranger's rules. Of course his ambition is to make his own in the world of entertainment and I wish him well in that.

Another sadness I have to report is that the spastic calf has died. He improved until he could stand and suck unsupported. I really thought, despite all that experience has taught me, that he might live. But then he started to lose condition and I started to lose heart.

The cow didn't though. She is the most patient beast I've known. She stood, without even a halter, for all the messing about with this calf and inexpert milkers taking extra for other calves. By the end she had developed a way of lying down beside him so that he could suck without getting up.

That was how I found him. Three weeks old, quite dead and with his mother's teat not five inches from his mouth, as she waited patiently for her calf to suck.

197

May 3, 1993

IACS forms not my idea of farming

THERE IS a worthy in the parish of whom it is said that he bought a fancy car in the days of the post-war boom, when farmers were expected to produce food and to be paid for it. It was a Daimler which had been chauffeur driven and, as such, had a glass panel between the front and back seats like a London taxi. The idea was that the chauffeur wouldn't be able to hear what his betters in the back were saying about his driving and the difficulty of getting decent servants these days.

Anyway, Jocky was conscious that the car was a bit grand for a farmer and he used to apologise for his extravagance by saying that it was handy because the glass panel stopped the calfies sucking your lugs.

I should have bought a car like that. It would have been a great help last Saturday.

At last I had found a calf to replace the spastic which died after all our attention and his mother's gallant attempts to let him suck by lying beside him. It was a Simmental bull, four days old and was to be had at Pirriesmill of Huntly.

The only snag I could see was the geography. My method of transporting calves is to bag them and put them in the back of the car. If I am getting them from a near neighbour I can sometimes get a calf all the way home before it escapes, but Huntly is thirty-two miles away.

The enormity of that led to the invention of an improvement in my transportation protocols. Having bagged him I then put him in a second bag and tied both tightly.

I don't know what Joanna Lumley would say about the method nor am I quite sure that it met fully with EEC Directive 27834018 but it worked. I got home with dry lugs for once and with hardly any calf scour under the hatchback.

Soon my gallant cow had a live calf that could stand and suck and suck and stand and then dance round the pen for the joy of it all, and of

being at Little Ardo.

I felt good about my farming that day.

That was nice for I had set last week aside for the final assault on my IACS form.

Filling in IACS forms is not my idea of farming. Indeed it is a nightmare. I can tell you that, with a fortnight to go, not one of the discussion group has finished his form and, if our experience is repeated nationally there there will be the biggest cock-up in bureaucratic history.

I am in deep trouble for one rather important thing. Because of boundary changes and building, accu-rate maps of Little Ardo as she is today, just do not exist. How then am I to get all my areas right?

A friend of a friend has decided to undo all the little bits of extensification that he had done over the last few years for the same reason. He had squared off all his irregular fields by planting trees in all the gushets. That was ideal for the wildlife as well as cutting down on the great EEC surpluses. But, of course, that put all his acreages wrong and rather than re-measure all his fields, or risk guessing wrongly, he has ploughed all his trees under.

I'm scared stiff. The cash I could lose is so much and my

record is so bad. I got in trouble last year because I couldn't account for a cow and I was fined for claiming three-quarters of an acre too much rape acreage, so what chance have I of getting all this lot right?

One of the things I must do is to be sure to sow all the acreages on the ordinance survey maps (where they are accurate). That means forcing the plough into all the dyke-sides and into those difficult areas we had been leaving to the wildlife. It may not be what is intended but it is what we are doing. I usually don't bother to sow the cornyard after the last bales are taken off it. That is a great source of seeds for the birds and the voles. But this year we have ploughed up every square yard.

Anyway, I have chickened out. Instead of tackling the form myself I have hired a member of the Green Wellie Brigade. He'll be well worth his eighteen pounds an hour if he gets my forms correct and in in time.

He was full of confidence when I hired him and none put off by the fact that the maps available only gave a historical record of the size and shapes of Little Ardo's fields.

That would be no problem, he would redraw them.

That must be a skill beyond price in these difficult times. But whether my man has the skills I don't yet know. It was all supposed to be done on Thursday and at eighteen pounds an hour, I would go to him...you can't have a valuable chap like that driving about in a car. But when we got to it he had only redrawn the bit where the new houses have been built and had done nothing about all the other incompatibilities between the ordinance survey and reality - so next week he is coming here.

He has promised not to go home before the form is filled and I can make him the same promise. I have plans to have his cylinder-head removed, for replacement when the job is done. Surely we'll make it even if we have to measure every field on the place.

I have no confidence, only this; my consultant has an insurance policy against cock-ups.

The boys in the discussion group have another source of comfort. The Department haven't got a snowball in hell's chance of sorting this lot out anyway.

May 10, 1993

Jolly nights and slow mornings

I THINK I could just about cope with my social life if it wasn't for the work I have to do as well.

It has been a busy time. We had the conception of a new grandchild to celebrate this week. Very nice that, the young couple being so pleased about the deal. They have so much control nowadays. Our grannies regarded the advent of children as something to be enjoyed or endured. In our own case we only just slipped back a few months a year until we had four and someone told us what was doing it. We soon stopped it then I can tell you. I don't remember any great celebrations of our conceptions.

But there's the Recovery Stock, with his restaurant providing the money for the booze, just effervescing with excitement at the prospect of reproduction.

Then we had to celebrate the visit of a rich aunt from London whose rich husband would buy us dinner. And again an old pal from the schooldays came visiting. He once gave me a thrashing in the Pleasure Park at Methlick. Bill Barclay has made good in Corby and tries to make up to me for that thrashing by taking us out for a meal every time he's home.

I caught sight of the bill on Friday night, "Good god Bill, That's a week's wages".

"Well Charlie, it may be a week's wages to you but it's nae for me and luckily I'm paying."

I couldn't argue with that.

One way or another there had been a week of jolly evenings and slow mornings by the time it came to Saturday night and a date with the current tenants of the farm on which my granny looked after me during the war. I was looking forward to something of a sentimental journey but I was so tired. I even fell asleep in the bath.

No one really understands if you call off on the grounds of tiredness so that was out. Off we went. It was wonderful to see the old place. This is the time of year

I liked it best; this was bird-nesting time. There wasn't time to go round the great hedge which ringed my granny's half-acre fruit garden, for we were soon partying.

Now, it's a funny thing but the more partying you do the less tired you get and the more you drink the thirstier you get. So the Farmer who went along dead tired for a couple of hours was in great fettle and most reluctant to let the Breadwinner take him home at two in the morning.

He would have been keener had he remembered about the alarm clock which was set for six.

And that's just the point. If I was Bertie Wooster I could handle the social life. If I had all day Sunday for the recovery, life would be a breeze. But on Sunday the beasts had to be seen to as usual. And the wheat had to sprayed. Mossie, who advises me on my spraying, was adament that the spray had to go on on Sunday morning - not afternoon.

I was soaking up a cup of tea while the sprayer filled again when the Breadwinner spoke and my heart sank. She was looking out of the window and over the fields to the little wood my grandfather planted in 1936. "Isn't the park beside the woodie set-aside?" she asked.

Indeed it was...or should have been. Ten cows and calves had somehow (quite easily in fact) got into this fine source of unmanured and lush grass. Worse than that they had got through that and onto a park of wheat.

It is virtually impossible for one man to drive ten cows through two narrow gates from a lush paddock onto a field that has been over-grazed. And yet I managed it. You have no idea the surge of energy it gives you and the speed that returns to tired and arthritic legs, when you envisage the man from the Department shaking his head and saying that you have lost all your lovely subsidies because you have been grazing your set-aside.

Mossie's really going to town on subsidy collection. His latest is sunflowers. He's so pleased with the first field that he's managed to find another to sow. "More happy faces" he says, "And do you see the weather since I put in my sunflowers? Not a drop of rain and sunshine every day" He's taking credit for the weather next. He may not be able to walk on water but he's trying to grow sunflowers on a bog which must be a farming equivalent.

Someone at the discussion group asked him why on earth sunflowers? What a daft question. There's an even bigger subsidy on them. There would need to be. There is even less chance of a harvest.

But then, that is how they are setting things up for us farmers. I ache for the days when we tried to produce food for a market.

Again it was Mossie who put that in perspective. I have as many as fifty beetles to the plant in my winter rape and was for spraying them. "Dinna bother," says Mossie, "What does it matter? They winna eat your forms."

True, true. So at least I didn't have to spray for beetles on Sunday. The last cow was calving though. A big Black Hereford with maybe a bit of Simmental, she was very late and, as she was coming on fast, I thought I'd just watch her. I got a bit bield at the side of the dyke and sat down in Sunday's glorious sunshine. I was needing the rest. Within what seemed like a few seconds I was awakened by a determined heaving sound from my cow. By the time I focused, the calf was out and the cow was up and licking it. It is the biggest bull calf of the season.

I hadn't been much of a cattleman but she'd managed without me. If I'm to keep up with my pleasures, more of the farm will have to be like her.

May 17, 1993

My euphoria lasted only for one day

THAT'S IT. Half the year's work done this week. The Forms are in.

I know loads of people who aren't going to make it and many more who say that it is a tremendous imposition on us. So it is, of course. They should just give us the money without putting us to all the trouble of filling in forms.

But the fact is that those of us who want the money are just going to have to fill them in. Once you accept that, it is a pretty good rate of pay. It cannot be more than two day's work for my small holding and yet my total subsidies should be £18,000 if I have filled in everything correctly. That is the greatest incentive I have ever had to do anything well in farming.

And that is where I fall out with the present system. It is rewarding me for filling in forms. How good it was in the old days when you got the money for being a good farmer. Now they will give us the cash for any half-decent attempt to grow crops and without worrying whether we can harvest them or not - provided your form is filled in correctly.

Having said all that, this money isn't for nothing. The bite is not yours until it's in your mouth. I know all about that for last year, when we only had to worry about forms for oil-seed rape, I was fined over five hundred pounds for making a wee arithmetical error. It was just bad luck that the error happened to be on my side.

They only check a random sample of claims but with my criminal record I am confident that I'll be in the random sample again this year so I have been very nervous about getting everything dead right.

It's not an easy job either. I have hired Green Wellies for nearly as much per hour as a washing machine repair man and I've tried to impress upon him the enormity of what I'll do with his bill if I am fined this year. And still I worry. When he had told me how much of the last field to leave in set-aside and how

204

much to sow in rape I said that, just to be safe, I would leave a little extra set-aside.

He just about hit the roof. "For god's sake don't do that. If you do you'll be below your rape acreages and you'll have over-claimed on your rape." I shudder to think what the penalty for a second offence is, and my misdemeaners would be consecutive at that.

Anyway, that was my plan. I would see to the farming and Green Wellies would fill in the forms. That has been done. I signed them last week and I was the first of the boys to get rid of my IACS.

The euphoria lasted for a day. I would put a few old cows over to the croft of the old widow-body who has let me graze her sixteen acres for the last four summers. It's very old Yorkshire foggage but, at one to the two acres, it would easily fatten some farrow cows. I was pleased that this year, under the new system, the croft would also count as forage acres - a bonus surely and quite unexpected.

But disaster struck. An indiscrete word about the grass needing renewing and I had lost it. If her grass wasn't good enough she would keep it - and she did.

Consternation in the Farmer's breast. The form is in and it's all wrong. The forage hectares are short of requirements. He had claimed for sixteen acres too much wheat and left two and a half acres too little set-aside.

"What can you expect. He did the same last year - and was fined for it. Off with his head."

Barlinnie loomed for the Farmer. The poor Breadwinner would come home to an empty house. Potions, the chemist who comes to help when he's not busy, would have to try to manage the farm between prescriptions and the Wasting Asset would start driving the Jag. How far would he get and how fast would he be going when he wrote it off? Would the insurance cover it?

I needn't have worried quite so much. Green Wellies soon had the form back from the Department and all the sums redone. The form didn't look so good with all the scored out bits and the tippex but at least I was all ready to deliver it on Wednesday morning.

As I waited my turn in the heaving queue at the Department I decided to have a look just to make sure that Green Wellies had got everything just right. A waste of time really. I had taken no interest and so had no chance of checking it properly.

Except - the farm number was wrong. And the widow-body's ground was still there. More tippex and we were right as rain except that I had forgotten the map. Fifty miles later I was back. After the man from the Department had tippexed out the red marks round the widow's croft the map was accepted, a receipt was given and the Farmer felt as free as air.

But I won't be happy till I've got the money.

Mind you, it will be a bit embarrassing if I do get all this money. And if I'm embarrassed what about Mossie? His subsides will be enough for any decent man to retire on. He's got four hundred acres of rape at two hundred pounds an acre for a start. And goodness knows what he's getting for his two fields of Happy Faces. In fact he's so embarrassed that he's off to the pig fair to see if he can get rid of some money.

Our good fortune is unlikely to last and Mossie is determined not to let the tax man get any.

I'm lucky there. I have so many losses carried forward from the bad times, that it will take some years of making subsidies while the sun shines before I have to pay Mr Lamont a penny.

Old bangers going into beef trade

THE BREADWINNER and I had words the other day. Like most words between people who have stuck it out together for a long time they weren't important nor do I even remember what they were supposed to be about. I do remember what I said though, and I am deeply ashamed. I made a sizist remark.

Having exhausted whatever case I had in logic, I resorted to naked abuse and said to her. "You were born wee, then you didna get far enough in about to the trough, that's your trouble."

It was a terrible thing to say and I cannot understand why I said it. After all, the two men whom I hold in the most awe were not big. One was my father who was an intellectual giant but only five foot eight...no more than average for his day. And the other was my headmaster, W.B.Curry who was four foot ten high and used to peer through the steering wheel of his giant Lagonda. I was terrified of Beakie Bill, as we called him, and yet he never once lifted a hand to anyone nor, as far as I am aware, ever punished a pupil in any way whatsoever.

Yet here I was putting the Breadwinner down for her shortness and she swears blind she is five foot two, almost. And I can't afford to have a real fall-out with the Breadwinner. It's not just that she is so good at winning bread, but she has also a half share in the farm. Imagine what would happen to my inheritance if she walked off with half of it?

Thank goodness I had the sense to give her the last word. "I did so, get up to the trough. They just didn't put much in it. That's all." she said pouting a bit.

I'm not one to complain about the weather, as you know, but really this is awful. I nearly lost a cow with worms and then, when she was on the mend but she was still short of milk, I lost her calf one coorse night. And we had a cow one frosty morning dead as a doornail with staggers where, twenty minutes earlier, I had seen her cavorting about as though with the joys of spring. That's the first cow we've lost to staggers since we started offering them magnesium syrup. Of course you can offer them magnesium but you can't force them to drink it.

Now, with all this cold, the grass is beginning to lose its battle with the cattle, the spring rape that was late in and thin sown is looking later and thinner.

Of course Mossie is quite right, it hardly matters what the crops themselves look like, but there is no subsidy on dead cows. On his entreaty I did try them, though. I rang up the Department of Agriculture and asked to speak to "Passport Control". Give him his due, my friendly man from the Department did laugh. He also laughed when I tried to persuade him that subsidising me to keep dead cattle would be no more silly than subsidising me to grow linseed on a North-East hillside nor for Mossie to get a fortune for growing his happy faces.

And one, smile deserves another. I asked Passport Control what I was supposed to do about the three steers which have lost their tags. If I heard right, he said that all I have to do is to put in another tag, score out the number on the CCD and write in the new number. I think we should be able to live with a passport

208

system that is as relaxed as that....there may be hope for the dead ones yet. It'll just take a bit of figuring out.

I should know a bit more about the system after Friday when I put twenty of last years bull calves to market. I was going to put them last week but Passport Control wouldn't let me because their residential qualification wasn't yet served.

I am looking forward eagerly to the sale. As I understand it, and I do not understand it well, I will get a large slice of £54 a head of subby and whatever they make in the ring, and that should be exciting. I had a look last week and anything you'd want to have about the place seemed to be making 150 pence a kilo, which is more than I've ever got. Indeed so wild has the demand become that I saw an old Limousine cow making £1100 in the sausages ring. And that's a lot of sausages.

Indeed I suspect that the old bangers are going into the beef trade. That seems bad. If beef is to stay dear, and we all pray it may, it can't be anything less than good. If people pay through the nose for beef like leather they won't be back to the butcher unless he keeps poultry.

Of course, it's just that the devaluation was so big and so quick. If we hadn't had the crazy idea that the value of the pound could be held steady for ever and it had drifted down slowly, the shortage wouldn't have happened. Those who found beef production impossible under the old prices would not have been forced out of business.

But let us not complain if things are uncommon good for us just now. After-all, there is no way it is going to last.

Big Hamish, who is big in the union as well as in himself, thinks it will last longer than anyone else I know. He reckons we have four years and then we'll be forced to compete on the world market.

I'm even more optimistic. The best explanation I have for the insanity of the Common Agricultural Policy is that it is designed to let the French and German peasants die off slowly. There are millions of them so they are politically powerful but their young folk are not staying on the land. My guess is that there will still be enough of them to keep the farce going for six years.

I do hope so. I have promised to retire in 1999.

Day a judge went into overdrive

IT'S HIGH time too, but the cattle job is a joy for sellers just now. And it's not just the usual spring madness which has pushed up the grass and pushed up the prices of the right type of store cattle towards the two pounds a kilo. Fat cattle are also at record levels and old cows for the sausage trade are at higher values at the end of their days than they ever were in their prime.

So the Farmer was in optimistic mood this week. He had twenty store cattle at handy weights and four two-year-old heifers to sell at Inverurie on Friday.

Potions the chemist helped me load my four-legged gold on Friday and when we put up the tail door of the float he turned and said, in the way that old men of the soil speak, "Aye Charlie, the only thing you can get wrong now, is to get Group 4 to take the cheque to the bank."

How wrong he was - how lacking in imagination. By the end of the day I was in constant fear of the police at the door.

It was to be my first experience of selling cattle with passports, but I had the documents and I had no reason to fear that anything would go wrong. I did though, and it did.

My first problem was that the seller before me in the ballot didn't turn up so my number came up fifty cattle (maybe twenty minutes) earlier than expected. I was through watching proceedings in another ring when a breathless young man came running through for me. Normally they'd have carried on without me but, in these days of CCDs, they do really like the seller there.

I explained that I'd been held up by Passport Control as I scuttled up holding my sheaf of forms, but it wasn't an ideal start.

And the sale didn't proceed uniquely well either.

The bullocks should really have been outside a month ago as it takes them three weeks to get used to the change in diet and by the time mine were used to the grass half of the best of the grazing season would be away. Not only that but they all seemed to be a hundredweight lighter than I expected. And then again I had forgotten that, among these fine steers, there were still three carrying Simmental markings but Jersey conformation.

It started well enough, with a Belgian Blue steer weighing nine hundredweight making £620, or 155 pence a kilo. Then a pair of Simmentals made156 pence and then one made 159 pence, or £640. This looked good. I can surely keep his mother for that and put the variable premium and the Hill Livestock Compensatory Amounts towards the expense of living.

Then came the Jerseys.

Now it is important to realise that selling store cattle is more than just a fund-raising exercise. It is a parade of your breeding skills. It is a testimony to your animal husbandry. If you have bad cattle you don't take them to the biggest market for miles around on its busiest day. The toe-rags must be kept at home until there is some fat on them and they can be sneaked off, direct to the bandits at the slaughterhouse.

They may give you less but that is the price of your shame.

My cattle were too late to market because they hadn't got their passports in order for an earlier sale. They hadn't been outside because I had to keep far too many cows to exploit the new EEC arrangements to the full and therefore had no grass. But I really couldn't blame anyone for these slatey-arsed brutes and was dismayed by the sight of them in the ring.

They did make 128 pence a kilo which would have been good another year and was very good for what they were.

But then the real disasters started.

My next steer had a very full scrotum for one who was alleged to have been castrated. Indeed he had been done with a bardizzo which cuts off the blood supply to the testicles rather than removing them and I was just about able to convince the auctioneer that it was indeed a steer. "Oh dear me, Yes. I'm always very careful about that sort of thing. You wouldn't get me selling a bull as a steer. Ho, ho,ho."

I would have held my tongue had I but known what was coming next. It had the opposite fault. Far from having too much masculinity it

211

had too little. "Now the last een. A heifer this time."

If I'd kept quiet I might have got away with it but I became flustered. I had a CCD for this animal. I had testified before God and Department of Agriculture that this was a boy-child born last year and eligible for up to £54 in subsidies.

The auctioneer became pleaded with him he wasn't going to let me withdraw my heifer from the sale. The law must take its course. Besides, the sale was going well. The buyers could see that they were onto a collector's item here. The first and only female holder of a CCD was coming under the hammer before their very eyes. Each man was but one wave from

the judge, the packed ringside became the public in the gallery come to see me get my just deserts for the heinous crime of defrauding the Common Agricultural Policy, obtaining passports fraudulently and wasting the time of public servants.

But the judge was into overdrive. No matter how I having ownership of the first CCD carrying heifer in the British Isles.

I got 153 pence for my heifer but I'm not going to try it again. I haven't slept a wink since and, by the time you're reading this, I'll have been onto the Department doing my Daft Willie act - again.

212

Argus has a gleam back in his eye

YOU KEN FINE WHIT TO DAE, DON'T YE ARGUS?

LA 93

ARGUS THE Simmental bull, has made a flying start to his year's work. He had had a three week warm-up with eight of my neighbour Gowkie's cows but, on the first, he went in with the hill cows here.

We had let him get far too thin by running him with the cows during the winter. They were asked to survive on syrup, straw and foggage until well into the new year, and, while most of them survived

and even thrived, poor old Argus lost weight when he should have been building up to his busy six weeks in early summer.

I suppose checking-out forty cows twice a day all winter on a diet of straw would be too much for any bull, but he was a poor specimen when we gave him a pen to himself in January.

He reminded me of what Gerry Rankine said to me when I bought a champion

Simmental bull in Edinburgh almost twenty years ago. It had been bred and pampered by Tom Barr of Hobsland in Ayrshire and had clearly wanted for nothing. As I admired my purchase Gerry said, "Aye, take a good look at him. He'll never look as well again." That rather unkind prophesy was absolutely correct. Indeed it took Columbus a week to realise that I was indeed serious. He was to survive on grass alone.

But, after three months of silage and cake, Argus improved greatly and, by the time he arrived back from his holidays among the old dears on the braes of Gowkstone, he was looking a picture. The ribs had disappeared, the coat had a gloss on it and there was a gleam in his eye.

He has only six weeks to get round forty-six of them (and remember last year he had Rastus the Black bull to help) so I'm glad to say that he got off to a flying start with three on his first afternoon home.

And Argus isn't the only one whose responsibilities grow daily. You'll remember Crookie, the Potato Baron, who spent the first thirty-nine years of his life promoting the interests of the Scottish malting barley industry. You'll also remember the

fears we had about ever seeing him again after he decided, last year, to take a wife.

Well, the wife's a Maitland and a distant relative of mine, so I guessed Crookie was going to find his freedom of action severely curtailed. I was absolutely right. She's fairly got him on a ball and chain. Every time he sneaks round the corner of the steading his Fiona puts on the brake and he finds himself spinning backwards towards the kitchen.

We miss Crookie at the discussion group that meets at the Salmon Inn on a Sunday night, but the lad himself is in his element. There is a race on to see which Crookie will become first, forty or a daddy....and the betting is five to four on the field.

Crookie wasn't even at the Scotsheep event which for some reason was held in Buchan where sheep are strangers and cattle have always been king. I remember my grandfather reacting sulkily when my grandmother served him mutton twice in successive weeks.

She tried to cajole him out of his truculence at this inferior fodder by saying to her guest "Maitland likes a bit of mutton, don't you dear?"

"I used to like it for a

change," he said.

It was a bit like the decision to send David Livingstone to preach about Christianity to the heart of a dark continent which had no shortage of gods of its own; it could work, but the odds were against it.

And against the odds Scotsheep does seem to have fulfilled most people's expectations. Something short of five thousand people turned up and saw demonstrations of what twenty-five breeds of sheep can do when they are crossed and recrossed.

Scotsheep was thought, by the practical men, to be more use than the Highland and other prestige shows because those concentrate so much on the pedigrees whereas, apart from the Blackies, the money is in getting the right cross. But it was a baffling occasion for a cattleman who has been brought up to regard people who grow sheep as brave and sturdy souls who are making the best of a bad job by putting on their land all that it is fit for.

As usual the boys were most at home in the bar, discussing the latest blunders by the government. And it was there that one of the sheepmen who had come all the way up to Buchan from Doonhame said, "Well, at least there is this, boys. We may have a lot of goats in the government but at least we've got a Shepherd for Minister of Agriculture."

Anyway, a jolly time was had by all.

Well nearly all. Big Hamish and Potions the chemist decided to go to a roup instead. Next time they'll go to Scotsheep.

Hamish was deep in conversation, while chewing his way through a can of lager, when out of the corner of his eye he spied a really substantial chain which had stuck at ten pounds. It was being held up by the assistant with two hands to show it off. He duly bought the chain only to discover that the head of a man who was standing in front of him had obscured the fact that it was not one nice long chain but two rather short bits of chain.

And then Potions tried to buy a compressor so that I could blow up the tyres of my tractors if I asked him nicely. Unfortunately he had not bought the compressor but a three and a half hundredweight anvil.

Meanwhile, back at the farm, Argus got quietly on with his work.

Mossie is Laird again at Moss-side

I'M IN an optimistic mood. Two people who are close to me are enjoying a triumph each. They are triumphs which only peasants like us can enjoy fully or fully understand. One has added another farm to the paternal acres and the other has done even better. He has bought the paternal acres back.

The first happy man is David Henderson, Scotland's oldest farmer. As you eat your toast this Monday morning he is entering his one hundred and fifth year. And he is entering it with the warm glow of a man who is setting about the planning of his cropping programme for a new farm.

David is a far out uncle. His wife was a cousin of an uncle of mine's wife. You might think that a tenuous relationship indeed, and it is true that, if his fame had been based on sheepstealing, I wouldn't have mentioned it, but it is good to contemplate another farm coming into the family.

It is even better to think that my love of the land and my pride in it might still be strong in fifty years time when I am entering my 105th year.

Old David says that he bought the farm because he must always be interested and he just didn't have enough to think about. He used to fatten six hundred cattle a year. He bought most of those through the ring at Laurencekirk Mart where he was chairman for many years.

But, about the time that he turned a hundred, he decided that the ringside was a bit too much for him and so he cut down. But he still had a thousand acres arable in the Howe o' the Mearns. And the new farm, Redmyre at Fordoun, is some of the best red clay in that most fertile of Howes.

He says it's been badly farmed though. It was let out for grazing and courses of cropping. Everything sooked out and nothing put back in. Now it is to return to the peasant's rule of land management; "spend money on the place as if you were going to die tomorrow but farm as though you were to live forever."

The banker has already been to see David about his five year plan which should just about take him into his twelfth decade.

The peasant's instinct for his land is something to do with continuity. This peasant likes to stand in the home fields which have had the best of our muck for a hundred and fifty years and think about my father cultivating by proxy, with one foot on the gate, a fag in his mouth and six men in the field. I like to remember my grandfather picking up a handful of the black loam behind the plough in springtime and letting it run sensuously through his fingers. And I worry about what my great-great-grandfather thought when the keystone he put up in the old barn in 1857 came crashing down, almost killing his progeny in the course of my improvements. It is the continuity, the stewardship, the handing on from generation to generation.

You don't often get so much stewardship and so little handing on as in David Henderson's case. I asked him if he thought land was a better investment than shares for example. "Oh no," he said, as though it wasn't a very smart question, "its just what I have always done and what I have always known."

I have a long standing farming friend who became a "name" in a syndicate at Lloyds of London. I know he wishes he had stuck to the peasant's approach to investment.

The other happy farmer is Mossie. Now, you might think the Grain Baron, who has bought a farm every now and every then for the last number of years, and who would need a better car if he were to get round all his farms in a day, would not be greatly affected by the addition of another to his empire. You'd be wrong though.

And you'd be wrong for a special reason. You see Mossie's purchase is Mossside of Tarves, where his father farmed before him.

He has owned it before, of course, but in the days when he had stoties. Funnily enough he wasn't any better at the stoties than the rest of us and, like the rest of us, he spent much of the time trying to get cash to flow uphill.

Unlike the rest of us though, he saw the light. Indeed he saw two lights at once. He saw that he had a

choice of being a working fool like me or a grain baron. And, if he was going to keep animals, it should be something that would be fed automatically and leave a small margin.

It was at that time that the financial institutions had the idea of going into land ownership in a big way. They bought up half the land about here and awaited eagerly the annual increase that this would afford them.

Mossie sold at a price which was as fair to himself as he could manage and set about spending the money on becoming a grain baron and swineherd. It was such a success that he was able to buy up several farms in the bad times that followed, as well as spending much more time

in the watering holes than had ever been possible when he was in beef.

Twelve years after the sale, he was able to buy Moss-side back. He is being a bit coy about the price but others have managed it for half price and Mossie likes to do better. And he has had the use of the money at four percent in the second worst period of inflation in the history of the country.

I don't suppose it was anything to do with those financial details and I am sure it was everything to do with the peasant's passion for his land, but they do say that the bottom lip was trembling when Mossie told his wife that his bid had been accepted and that he was Laird again at Moss-side.

Hiding my shame from Grain Baron

THE SCOPE for poisoning yourself keeps rising and, if it is rising for everyone, it is rising especially for me. I am not only doing my spraying these days but I am enjoying spraying and like to do it as often as economics will allow.

If you are going to spray chemicals on someone else's fields you have to go away on courses on safety. You learn all about wearing gloves, goggles and breathing masks. You also learn what to do if by any mischance there should be any contact between any chemical and yourself.

But as I only spray at Little Ardo I am allowed to poison, burn and choke myself as much as I like.

When I started spraying two years ago I took full advantage of that dispensation but I have decided that that was not wise. I don't appear to have done any permanent damage yet but I have given myself a number of headaches when spraying without a mask on and the back window open. That works alright when you are going against the wind but if you are going with the wind a cloud of spray follows you and can be quite choking. It can also give you a nasty skin rash.

So I am getting round to safety first in spraying. Last year I bought the masks, the gloves and the boilersuit. This year I have made a start to wearing them...at least I put on the rubber gloves and the boilersuit this week.

It was a start but I am sorry to say that it was not a great success.

My old friend Sandy Fowlie who has kept cattle all his days and has even made money out of them, told me the other day that I would have to stop telling everyone of my mistakes because they might begin to think I wasn't very clever. My attitude is that if I tell you about my occasional disaster you will believe me if I ever have a triumph to report. I don't want to be like Mossie who has so many triumphs that everyone just thinks he's blawin.

The truth will out.

Almost the first act in my new safety-first regime was to pour the Twerp-All into the sprayer. That's a most important spray according to Mossie. It is critical that it be done in exactly the right proportions within six hours of the plant reaching growth stage thirty-two.

Anyway there I was with this five-litre can of Twerp-All, feeling a bit of a banana in my yellow boilersuit and a bit of a cissie with my rubber gloves, when Mossie arrived in the close.

He always makes me nervous and it may have been something to do with that, I don't know, but my boilersuit has great baggie sleeves and I suddenly felt my arm engulfed in a searing cold flood which had reached my chest in no time and trickled slowly down to my naval and beyond. I had somehow managed to pour the Twerp-All down the sleeve as much as into the tank.

Fortunately the stuff doesn't seem to be very corrosive for no ill-affects have yet shown up. It could have been bad though, because, even if it had been caustic soda, I'd have had to grin and bear it. I couldn't have let the Grain Baron see my shame.

If I'm going through a bad patch, Mossie's still on a

220

high. Not only has he completed the liberation of the family farm, back out of the clutches of the insurance company, but the new High Health piggies are breeding like rabbits and growing like mushrooms. He was onto the banker the other day and told him to brace himself for the deluge of cash that was about to hit Moss-side.

Now you can believe all that if you like but even I, who revere his wisdom, and am in awe of his strength of personality, am beginning to suspect Mossie just might be coming-it a bit over his sunflowers.

His 'Happy Faces' as he calls them are becoming an obsession. Luckily (and luckily for the rest of the family who find it hard to be enthusiastic about them all the time) two-year-old Jill is so very impressed with the Happy Faces that she has to be taken to see them twice a day.

Down they go to what used to be the moss, while the farmer explains to his youngest, that these are the tallest plants ever to be sown on the farm. There is a set of pylons which come striding through the moss and he explains that the Happy Faces will soon be up to the wires.

Jill is impressed but the Hydro-Electric weren't quite so sure when he phoned up to tell them they should heighten the wires, just in case.

Certainly they haven't done it yet, and I think they're quite right not to panic. I'm amazed how well the sunflowers have established in this far Northern clime and I suppose they could be four inches high already. But at that rate they'll take about fifteen months to reach the five feet high that a reasonable man might expect.

The Happy Faces are just another EEC scandal. The moss is ideal for birdies and frogs. Only the EEC could create conditions for the growing of linseed last year and now, with the mega subby, sunflowers. They can hardly grow them in Kent so what is Mossie doing growing them on Scotland's cold shoulder?

Anyway I'm giving six to four against him having a harvest of any kind, seven to two against him getting his seed back, and a hundred to one against him getting enough to justify the Happy Faces if you take away the area payments.

If he manages the sunflower in the moss we're going to get Mossie to take up, as his next challenge, growing winter wheat on a billiard ball.

221

Also available from Ardo

Green Heritage

*This novel was written in the early thirties by
John R. Allan. A successful young London business man
discovers his roots in North East Scotland.
Price now £9.95*

A Lucky Chap

*The autobiography of Sir Maitland Mackie, who with his father
founded what has become the biggest farming business in
Scotland. It recalls his upbringing on the farm at Tarves. It also
tells about his time as the Queen's representative
in Aberdeenshire and how he got on with the Royals.
It tells mostly of eighty years of fun.
Price still £12.50.*

A Desert Rat
in Holburn Street

*This is the life story of an Aberdeenshire lad who joined up
in the second world war and quicklyfound himself
in the desert war. He drove tanks in North Africa,
Italy and France and stayed alive when so many
of his comrades died. After the war he built up successful
grocery businesses in Holburn Street, Aberdeen
Price now £9.95*

Farmer's Diary

Charlie Allan records his struggles following his return to the family farm in 1989 after three years in Kenya's Happy Valley. He tells how he got the farm going again, tried to keep the banker happy and re-established a place in the small North East community of Methlick. This volume covers a long year to Christmas 1990. Illustrations are by Jim Turnbull. Price still £12.50

Volume II

Charlie continues his record of the never-ending battle with the weather and beaurocracy. He recounts the fun had by Mossie, Red Rooster and the other lads of the discussion group who meet at the Salmon Inn on a Sunday night to blow about their crop yields or drown their sorrows when the weather wins. This volume covers the year 1991 and up to end February 1992. Illustrations again by Jim Turnbull. Price now £9.95

Volume IV

Volume IV is already written and will be available to solve your Christmas gift problems of 1995.

All titles available at bookshops
throughout the North East
or direct from Methlick
Please add £1 for postage

Ardo Publishing Company Ltd.
Methlick, Aberdeenshire AB41 0HR
Tel/Fax 01651 806218